SCHOLA

GCSE 9–1 GEOGRAPHY AQA EXAM PRACTICE

Dan Cowling,
Philippa Conway-Hughes,
Natalie Dow and
Lindsay Frost

Authors:
Dan Cowling, Philippa Conway-Hughes, Natalie Dow:
The challenge of natural hazards
Physical landscapes in the UK
Urban issues and challenges
Fieldwork and geographical enquiries

Lindsay Frost:
The living world
The changing economic world
The challenge of resource management
Issue evaluation

Editorial team Haremi Ltd
Series designers emc design ltd
Typesetting York Publishing Solutions Pvt. Ltd.
Illustrations York Publishing Solutions Pvt. Ltd.
App development Hannah Barnett, Phil Crothers and Haremi Ltd

Designed using Adobe InDesign
Published by Scholastic Education, an imprint of Scholastic Ltd, Book End, Range Road, Witney, Oxfordshire, OX29 0YD
Registered office: Westfield Road, Southam, Warwickshire CV47 0RA
www.scholastic.co.uk

Printed by Bell & Bain Ltd, Glasgow

1 2 3 4 5 6 7 8 9 7 8 9 0 1 2 3 4 5 6

British Library Cataloguing-in-Publication Data
A catalogue record for this book is available from the British Library.
ISBN 978-1407-17684-0

Notes from the publisher
Please use this product in conjunction with the official specification and sample assessment materials. Ask your teacher if you are unsure where to find them.

The marks and star ratings have been suggested by our subject experts, but they are to be used as a guide only.

Answer space has been provided, but you may need to use additional paper.

Colour versions of the images and the answers for the practice papers in this book are available online. Visit: www.scholastic.co.uk/gcse

Contents

Topic 6

THE CHALLENGE OF RESOURCE MANAGEMENT

How to use this book

This Exam Practice Book has been produced to help you revise for your 9–1 GCSE in AQA Geography. Written by experts and packed full of exam-style questions for each subtopic, along with full practice papers, it will get you exam ready!

The best way to retain information is to take an active approach to revision. Don't just read the information you need to remember – do something with it! Transforming information from one form into another and applying your knowledge will ensure that it really sinks in. Throughout this book you'll find lots of features that will make your revision practice an active, successful process.

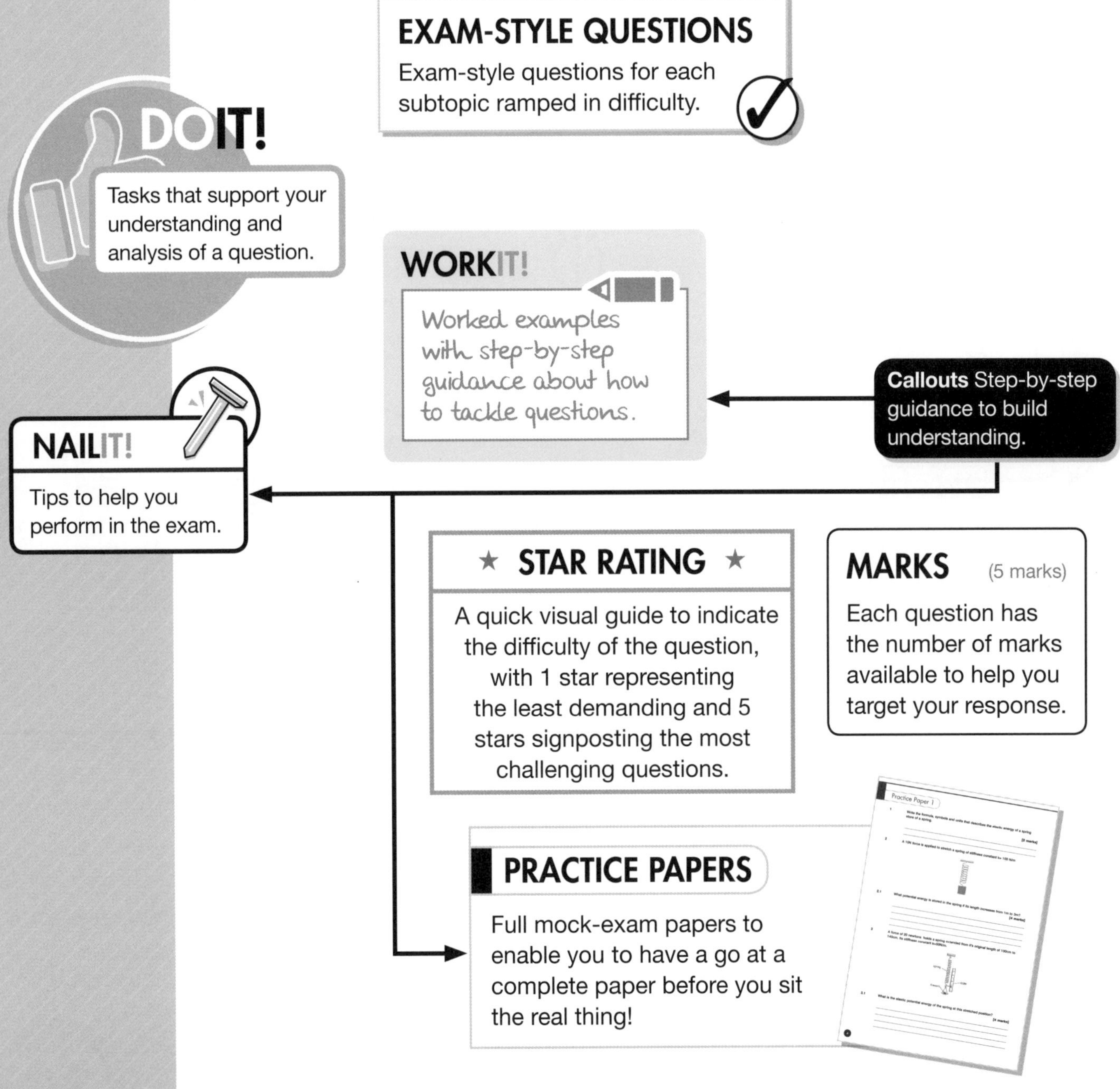

EXAM-STYLE QUESTIONS
Exam-style questions for each subtopic ramped in difficulty.
DO IT!
Tasks that support your understanding and analysis of a question.
WORK IT!
Worked examples with step-by-step guidance about how to tackle questions.
Callouts Step-by-step guidance to build understanding.
NAIL IT!
Tips to help you perform in the exam.
STAR RATING
A quick visual guide to indicate the difficulty of the question, with 1 star representing the least demanding and 5 stars signposting the most challenging questions.
MARKS (5 marks)
Each question has the number of marks available to help you target your response.
PRACTICE PAPERS
Full mock-exam papers to enable you to have a go at a complete paper before you sit the real thing!
Practice Paper 1

Use the AQA Geography Revision Guide alongside the Exam Practice Book for a complete revision and practice solution. Written by subject experts to match the new specification, the Revision Guide uses an active approach to revise all the content you need to know!

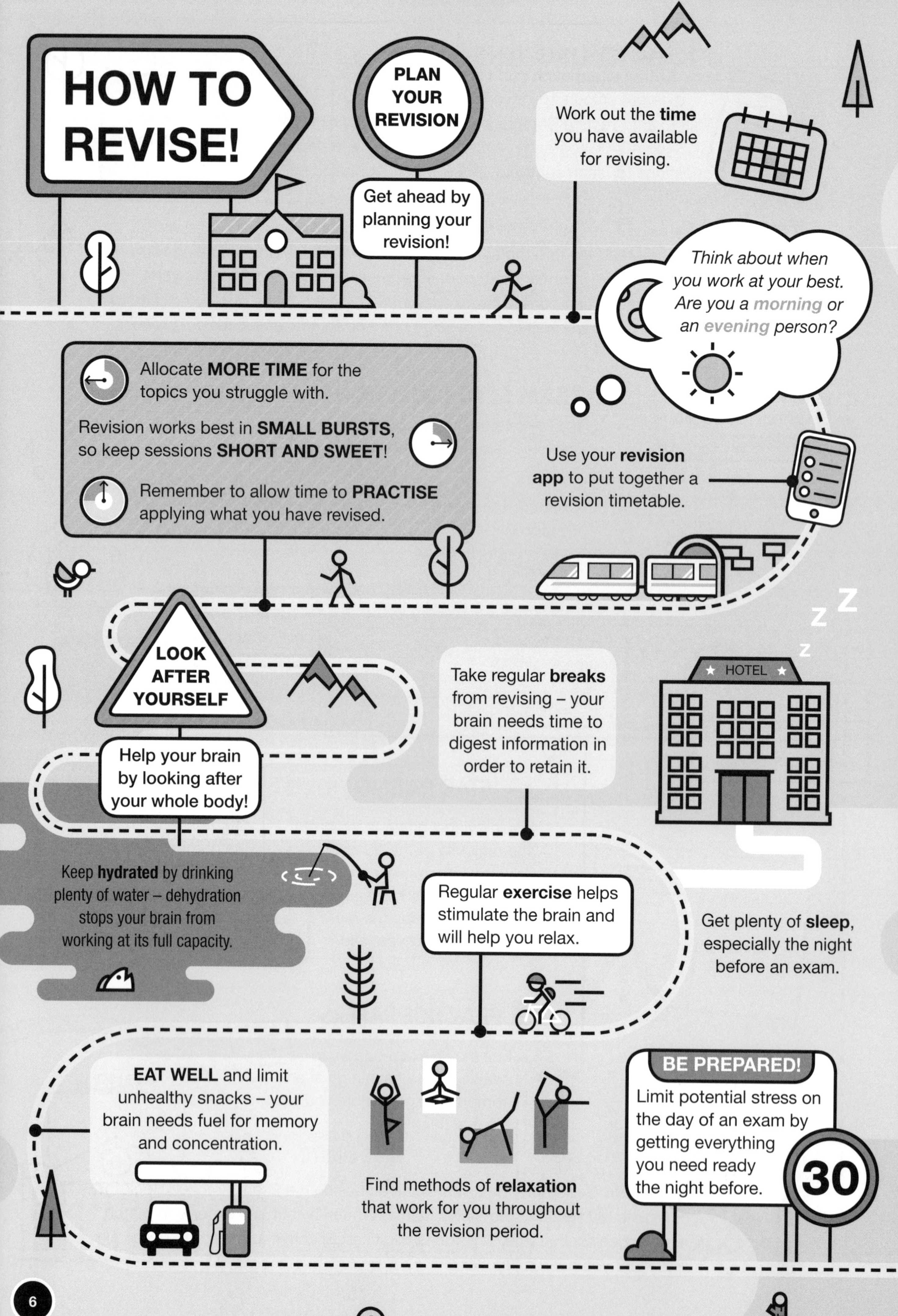
HOW TO REVISE!
PLAN YOUR REVISION
Get ahead by planning your revision!
Work out the **time** you have available for revising.
*Think about when you work at your best. Are you a **morning** or an **evening** person?*
Allocate **MORE TIME** for the topics you struggle with.
Revision works best in **SMALL BURSTS**, so keep sessions **SHORT AND SWEET**!
Remember to allow time to **PRACTISE** applying what you have revised.
Use your **revision app** to put together a revision timetable.
LOOK AFTER YOURSELF
Help your brain by looking after your whole body!
Take regular **breaks** from revising – your brain needs time to digest information in order to retain it.
HOTEL
Z Z Z
Keep **hydrated** by drinking plenty of water – dehydration stops your brain from working at its full capacity.
Regular **exercise** helps stimulate the brain and will help you relax.
Get plenty of **sleep**, especially the night before an exam.
EAT WELL and limit unhealthy snacks – your brain needs fuel for memory and concentration.
Find methods of **relaxation** that work for you throughout the revision period.
BE PREPARED!
Limit potential stress on the day of an exam by getting everything you need ready the night before.
30

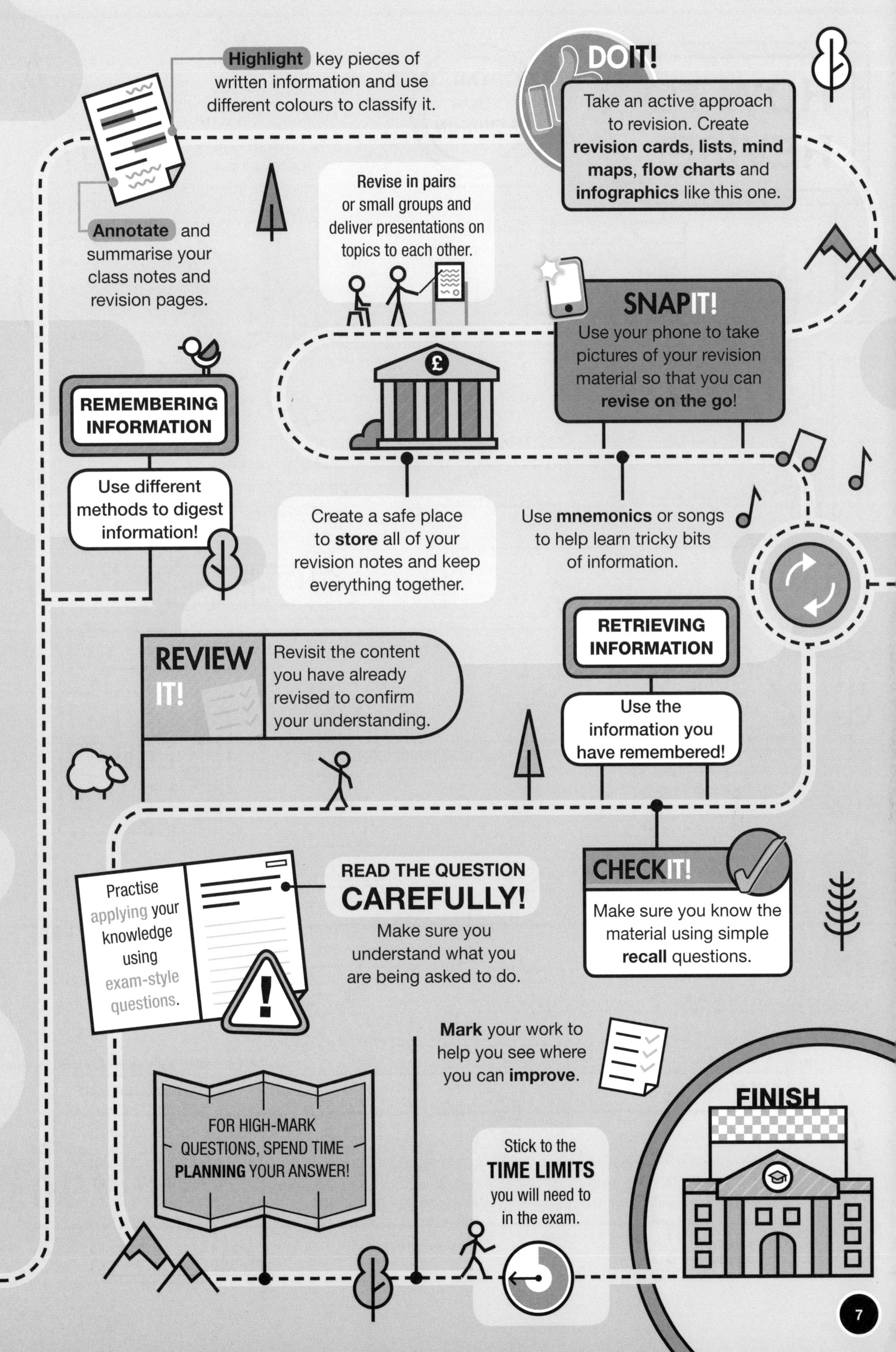

Highlight key pieces of written information and use different colours to classify it.
DO IT!
Take an active approach to revision. Create revision cards, lists, mind maps, flow charts and infographics like this one.
Annotate and summarise your class notes and revision pages.
Revise in pairs or small groups and deliver presentations on topics to each other.
SNAP IT!
Use your phone to take pictures of your revision material so that you can revise on the go!
REMEMBERING INFORMATION
Use different methods to digest information!
Create a safe place to store all of your revision notes and keep everything together.
Use mnemonics or songs to help learn tricky bits of information.
REVIEW IT!
Revisit the content you have already revised to confirm your understanding.
RETRIEVING INFORMATION
Use the information you have remembered!
CHECK IT!
Make sure you know the material using simple recall questions.
Practise applying your knowledge using exam-style questions.
READ THE QUESTION CAREFULLY!
Make sure you understand what you are being asked to do.
Mark your work to help you see where you can improve.
FOR HIGH-MARK QUESTIONS, SPEND TIME PLANNING YOUR ANSWER!
Stick to the TIME LIMITS you will need to in the exam.
FINISH

The challenge of natural hazards
Tectonic hazards

Study **Figure 1**, a world map showing the distribution of earthquakes and volcanoes.

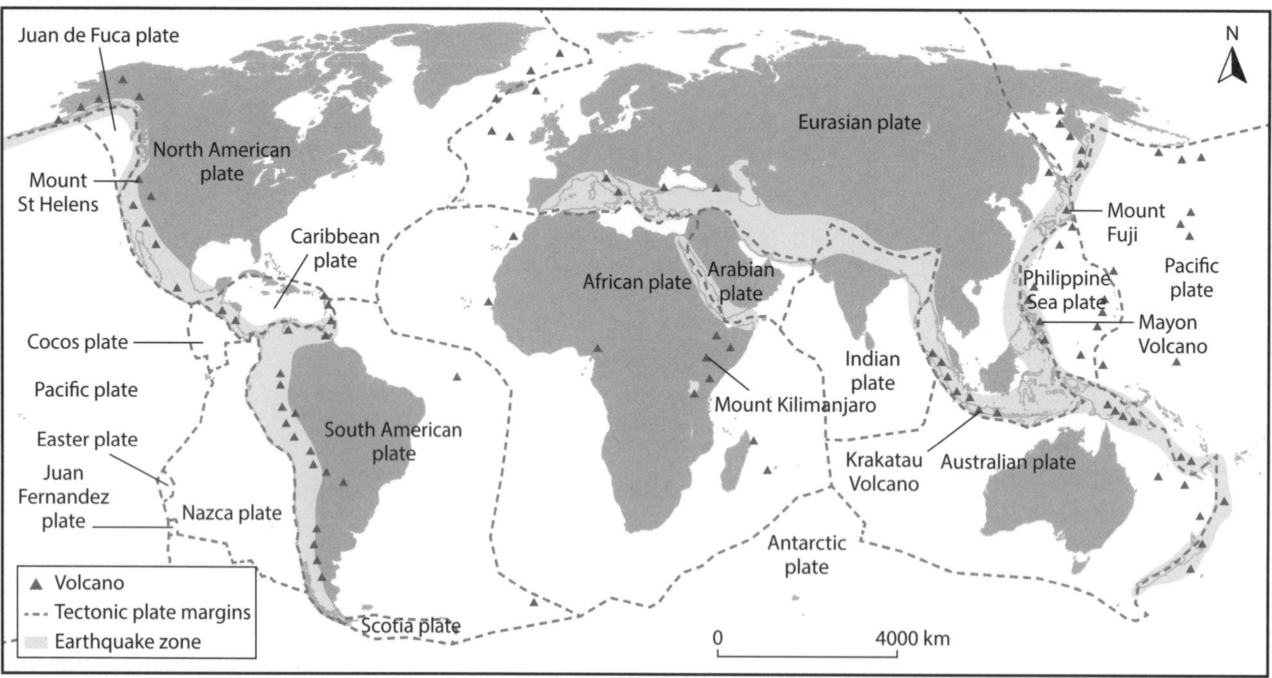

Figure 1

① Describe the distribution of earthquake zones shown in **Figure 1**. (2 marks, ★)

....

....

....

....

② Outline **one** reason why earthquakes are found in this pattern. (2 marks, ★)

....

....

....

....

NAILIT!

Outline

The command word *outline* means that in your answer you must provide a brief account of relevant information. There is a wide range of geographical factors and processes that could be tested with this type of question, but the answers do not require expansion.

3 Explain why volcanoes are formed at destructive plate margins. (4 marks, ★★★)

....

....

....

....

....

....

....

....

NAIL IT!

Make sure you learn the physical processes happening at each of the three types of plate margin and the landforms that are created. You could draw a flow diagram or a sequence of annotated diagrams in your revision. Include key terms and what they mean.

4 Explain **two** ways in which people can be protected from an earthquake. (4 marks, ★★)

Protection 1: ....

....

....

....

Protection 2: ....

....

....

....

DO IT!

Reducing the risk of tectonic hazards

Make sure you understand how monitoring, prediction, protection and planning can all reduce the risks of tectonic hazards. Commit to memory how different countries use these four management strategies.

5 Using a named example, describe the primary and secondary effects of an earthquake. (6 marks, ★★★)

....

....

....

....

....

....

....

....

....

....

....

....

WORKIT!

To what extent is it safe to live in an area at risk from a tectonic hazard? (9 marks + 3 SPaG marks, ★★★★★)

'To what extent' questions require you to judge the importance or success of a situation. You need to offer both advantages and disadvantages in your answer.

How to tackle a 'to what extent' question:

Step 1 Give two or three reasons why it may be safe to live in an area at risk from a tectonic hazard, such as Japan.

Step 2 Extend your points by explaining them.

Step 3 Try to include an example to support your point, for example, countries such as Japan have built earthquake-proof buildings.

Step 4 Repeat steps 1–3 for costs of living in an area at risk from a tectonic hazard.

Step 5 Give a conclusion as to whether you think it is safe or not.

This is a longer written answer and not necessarily straightforward. It may be advisable to make a brief plan for your answer in any available space on the exam paper, to help you link a sequence of points in a fluent way.

NAILIT!

Spelling, punctuation and grammar (SPaG) marks

In the longer answer questions, you will be assessed on your ability to present a fluent answer using correct spelling and punctuation, good-quality grammar (such as sentence structure) and geographical terminology. Make sure that you have prepared for this. Sometimes it can make a difference of a grade!

Weather hazards

Figure 2 shows the aftermath of a tropical storm.

Figure 2

Remember, answering multiple-choice questions should be quick. Aim to spend no more than 1 minute of exam time to work out the answer to this type of question.

(1) Which **two** statements about tropical storms are true?

Shade **two** circles only. (2 marks, ★)

A Tropical storms develop over the equator. ◯

B Tropical storms form above warm oceans (27°C or above). ◯

C Tropical storms gain energy as they hit land. ◯

D The conditions in the eye of the storm are calm. ◯

E Tropical storms only develop between August and October. ◯

(2) Outline **one** effect of a tropical storm. (2 marks, ★)

....

....

....

....

(3) Describe **two** ways that people can prepare for a tropical storm. (4 marks, ★★)

Preparation 1: ....

....

....

....

Preparation 2: ....

....

....

....

DOIT!

Primary and secondary effects

Make sure you understand the difference between primary and secondary effects. Commit to memory the primary and secondary effects of the different natural hazards, such as tropical storms. Learn your case studies!

WORKIT!

Explain how climate change might affect tropical storms. (4 marks, ★★★)

With an 'explain' question, you need to make a point and then give reasons for it. Answers should apply understanding of how climate change can affect a tropical storm – you will not get more than two marks if you only describe how they might change.

How to tackle this question:

Step 1 Describe one way that climate change could affect tropical storms: for example, warmer oceans.

Step 2 Apply understanding by explaining the impact of warmer oceans: for example, warmer oceans may increase the likelihood and intensity of tropical storms.

Step 3 Repeat steps 1–2 with a second point.

4. For a named tropical storm, assess the extent to which primary effects are more significant than secondary effects.

   Use a separate sheet of paper to write your answer to this question. (9 marks + 3 SPaG marks, ★★★★★)

5. Using a named example or case study, assess the impacts of a recent flood in the UK. (6 marks, ★★★★★)

NAILIT!

Make sure you learn your named examples or case studies so you can provide specific examples to support your answers.

....

....

....

....

....

....

....

....

....

....

....

6. 'The UK's weather is becoming more extreme.'

   To what extent is this statement true?

   Use a separate sheet of paper to write your answer to this question. (9 marks + 3 SPaG marks, ★★★★★)

NAILIT!

To what extent...?

The command phrase in this nine-mark question is *to what extent...?* In your answer, do not just describe and explain – you must also make a judgement on the truth of the situation identified by the question.

Climate change

Study **Figure 3**, a photograph of a volcanic eruption.

Figure 3

1. Describe **one** way in which volcanic eruptions can affect climate change. (2 marks, ★)

....

....

....

....

2. State **two** forms of mitigation to manage climate change. (2 marks, ★)

Form 1: ....

....

Form 2: ....

....

NAILIT!

State

The command word *state* is an alternative to 'give' or 'name'. You need to provide a basic response. In some instances, this may be a single word or phrase.

3. Explain the enhanced greenhouse effect. (4 marks, ★★★)

....

....

....

....

....

....

....

....

NAILIT!

A four-mark question is always point marked. This means that you need to give two points and develop them.

4 Explain the natural causes of climate change. (4 marks, ★★★)

....

....

....

....

....

....

5 Explain how human activity has contributed to climate change. (6 marks, ★★★)

....

....

....

....

....

....

....

....

....

....

NAILIT!

Explain

The command word *explain* is asking you to give reasons for something happening. In Question 5, you need to set out the human causes of climate change and show an understanding of how these activities affect the climate.

WORKIT!

Using named examples, assess the importance of local actions in reducing climate change. (9 marks + 3 SPaG marks, ★★★★★)

An 'assess' question requires you to make an informed judgement. You need to offer **both advantages** and **disadvantages** in your answer.

How to tackle this 'assess' question:

Step 1 Give three ways in which local actions have been effective.

Step 2 Extend your points by explaining how the local actions have been successful.

Step 3 Try to include an example to support each point.

Step 4 Repeat steps 1–3 to explain why global actions are also important in reducing climate change.

Step 5 Add a conclusion to say whether you think local actions can be a success on their own.

The living world
Ecosystems

Study **Figure 1**, which shows a nutrient cycle.

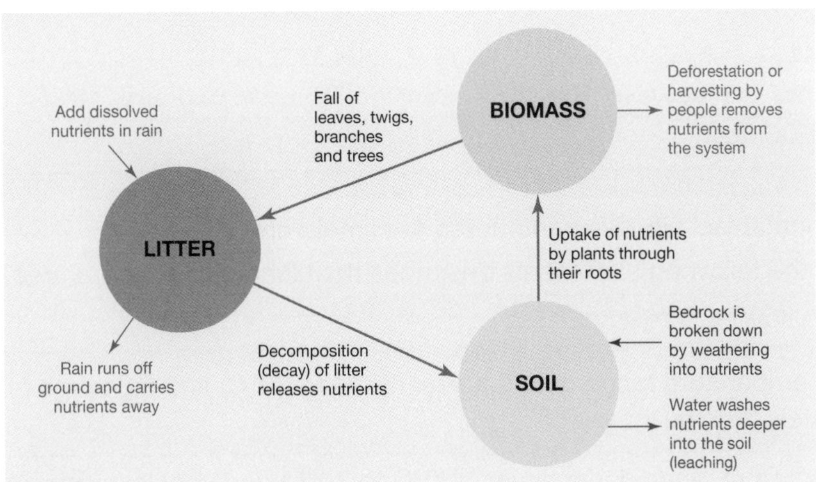

Figure 1

1. Using **Figure 1**, which **one** of the following statements is correct?
   Shade **one** circle only. (1 mark, ★)

   A Nutrients are added to the litter by run-off. ○

   B Biomass increases as leaves, twigs and branches fall to the ground. ○

   C Soils get nutrients from the decomposition of litter. ○

   D Deforestation adds nutrients to the soil. ○

2. Describe the role of water in the nutrient cycle shown in **Figure 1**. (2 marks, ★)

   ....

   ....

   ....

   ....

WORKIT!

Study **Figure 2**, which shows the Hadley convection cell in the atmosphere.

Describe the weather and climate conditions found at the equatorial location of tropical rainforests shown in **Figure 2**. (2 marks, ★)

How to tackle this question

- When asked to 'describe' something, you should give the main characteristics of it, in this case, of the weather and climate in tropical rainforest regions. No explanation is required.

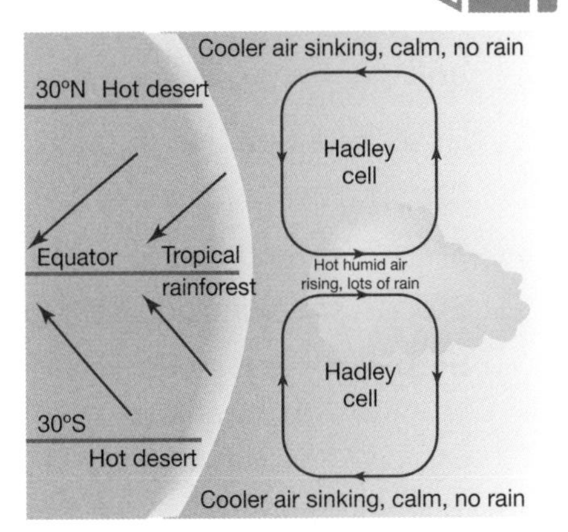

Figure 2

- Study **Figure 2** carefully and use the labels and annotations on the diagram to help you answer the question, along with what you have learned.
- In short-answer questions, the number of marks indicates how many points you should make in your answer. So, two good points here will secure the two marks available.

The climate is hot and humid all year with very little temperature range. Temperatures are usually over 25°C every day, with annual rainfall totals of around 2500 mm.

3. Which **one** of the following statements describes the climate of a tundra area? Shade **one** circle only. (1 mark, ★)

A Very small temperature range during a year (27°C to 30°C) and high precipitation (approximately 2500 mm a year). ○

B Small temperature range during a year (20°C to 30°C) and very low precipitation (approximately 125 mm a year). ○

C Large temperature range during a year (−25°C to +10°C) and low precipitation (approximately 500 mm a year). ○

D Moderate temperature range during a year (5°C to 18°C) and moderate precipitation (approximately 1500 mm a year). ○

NAIL IT!

Always read questions carefully to make sure that you actually answer the question. For example, do not muddle 'small-scale' with 'large-scale', or 'local ecosystem' with 'global ecosystem'.

4. For a small-scale UK ecosystem you have studied, describe and explain how the natural parts are linked together. (6 marks, ★★★)

Chosen small-scale UK ecosystem: ....

Describe and explain

Define what is meant by the command words *describe* and *explain*. If both are included in a question, you must do both to get all of the marks.

5. For a small-scale UK ecosystem you have studied, describe and explain how the natural balance may be changed. (6 marks, ★★★)

   Chosen small-scale UK ecosystem: ....

6. For the global ecosystems you have studied, to what extent do the interactions between the biotic and abiotic parts create a balance within the ecosystems?

   Use a separate sheet of paper to write your answer to this question. State your chosen global ecosystems at the start of your answer. (9 marks + 3 SPaG marks, ★★★★★)

Spelling, punctuation and grammar (SPaG) marks

In the longer answer questions, you will be assessed on your ability to present a fluent answer using correct spelling and punctuation, good-quality grammar (such as sentence structure) and geographical terminology. Make sure that you have prepared for this. Sometimes it can make a difference of a grade!

Tropical rainforests

1. Which **one** of the following statements describes a physical characteristic of a tropical rainforest? Shade **one** circle only. (1 mark, ★)

   A Soils are very fertile with lots of nutrients. ○

   B There are two layers of vegetation in the structure. ○

   C The growing season is eight months a year. ○

   D Nutrient cycling is very fast. ○

Study **Figure 3**, a photograph of young oil palm trees, planted after deforestation in Malaysia.

Figure 3

2. For a tropical rainforest you have studied, describe and explain the causes of deforestation. (6 marks, ★★★)

   Chosen tropical rainforest: ....

   ....
   ....
   ....
   ....
   ....
   ....
   ....
   ....
   ....
   ....
   ....
   ....

NAIL IT!

Make sure that you know the difference between *causes* of deforestation and the *ways* in which deforestation occurs. *Causes* refers to the underlying motives or reasons behind removing trees, rather than the methods or ways in which the trees are removed (such as by logging, road building, HEP construction, farming – although these will be mentioned within the sentences giving the reasons why these human activities are happening). Motives include overcoming poverty and making money for businesses or a country.

Study **Figure 4**, which shows indigenous territories and protected natural areas in countries with tropical rainforest in the Amazon region.

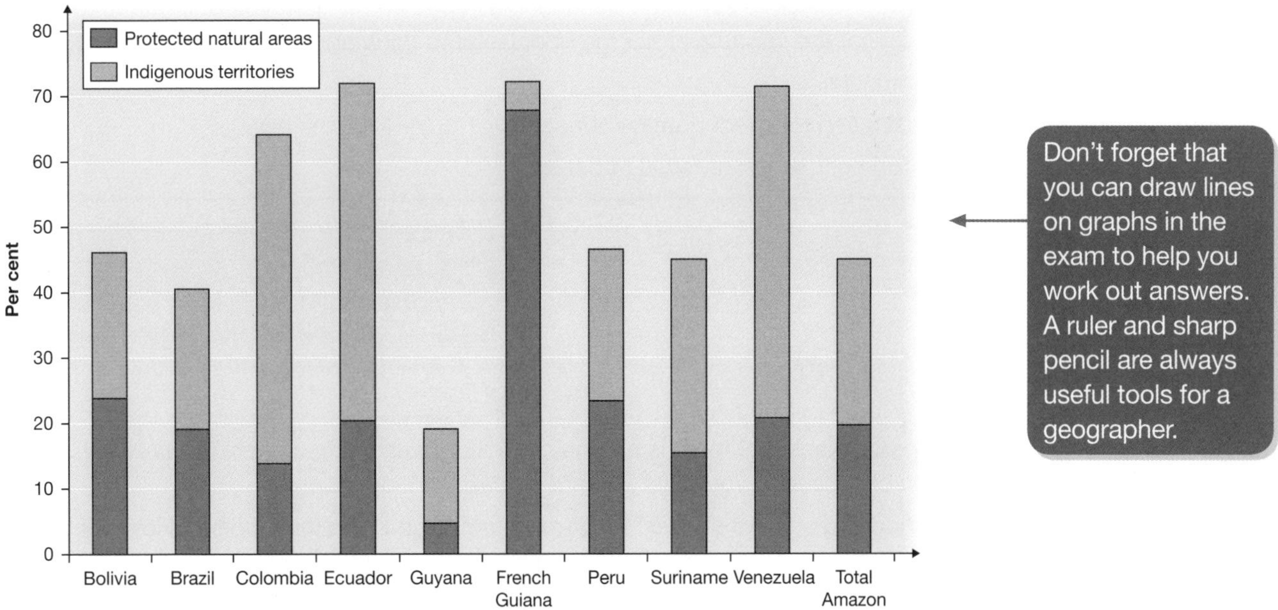

Don't forget that you can draw lines on graphs in the exam to help you work out answers. A ruler and sharp pencil are always useful tools for a geographer.

Figure 4

NAIL IT!

Make sure that you know how to read and interpret compound and divided bar graphs. For example, these questions require you to measure only the relevant shaded or coloured section and compare this with the relevant axis scale.

3 Which country has the largest percentage of protected natural areas? (1 mark, ★)

....

4 State the number of countries with 30% or more as indigenous territories. (1 mark, ★)

....

5 Outline **one** possible value to people of the tropical rainforest global-scale ecosystem. (2 marks, ★)

....

....

....

....

6 Outline **one** negative impact of deforestation in an area of tropical rainforest you have studied. (2 marks, ★)

....

....

....

NAILIT!

Many geography questions will ask you about impacts (effects). Remember that impacts can be positive (good) or negative (bad), so always check to see if the question has specified which type of impacts to consider. When thinking about what the impacts are, it may be useful to think about three categories:

- impacts on people (social impacts)
- impacts on money, businesses and jobs (economic impacts)
- impacts on the natural environment (environmental impacts).

The judgement you make is not right or wrong – it's what you think based on geographical ideas and information.

Suggest

The command word *suggest* means that there is no one correct answer. Instead, there are several possibilities from which to choose, and you must present a possible case for one.

Study the following question and student answer. What mark would you give the student? How could the answer be improved?

Suggest **one** way in which replanting trees can help make tropical rainforests more sustainable. (2 marks, ★★★)

Replanting trees makes the forest bigger so that there are more plants and animals.

7 Suggest **one** way in which education of people about conservation can help make tropical rainforests more sustainable. (2 marks, ★★★)

....

....

....

....

8 For a tropical rainforest you have studied, explain to what extent this ecosystem provides both opportunities and challenges for development. (9 marks + 3 SPaG marks, ★★★★★)

Use a separate sheet of paper to write your answer to this question. State your chosen tropical rainforest at the start of your answer.

NAILIT!

To what extent...?

The command phrase in this nine-mark question is *to what extent...?* In your answer, do not just describe and explain – you must also make a judgement on the importance or success of the situation identified by the question.

Hot deserts

Answer **either** questions on Hot desert environments **or** questions on Cold environments.

Study **Figure 5**, which shows a climate graph for a hot desert environment.

You will have studied *either* Hot desert environments *or* Cold environments. In the exam do **not** answer questions on both.

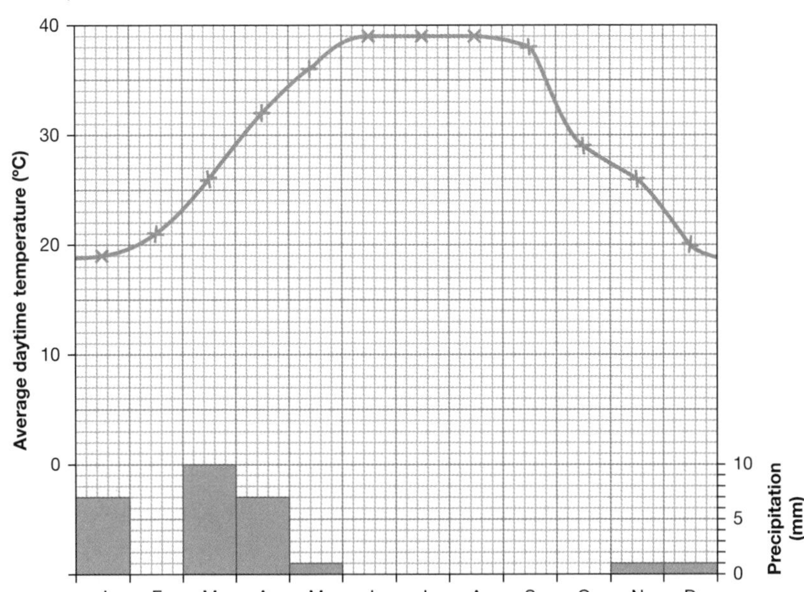

Figure 5

1. Using **Figure 5**, which one of the following temperatures is the correct average monthly temperature for October?

   Shade **one** circle only. (1 mark, ★)

   A 39°C ◯

   B 32°C ◯

   C 29°C ◯

   D 26°C ◯

NAILIT!

In questions that require you to write a number as an answer you should **always give the units** for a complete answer. For example, rainfall (or precipitation) is measured in millimetres (mm).

2. Using **Figure 5**, state the average total rainfall for January. (1 mark, ★)

NAILIT!

Outline

The command word *outline* means that in your answer you must state the main characteristics of something. There is a wide range of geographical factors and processes that could be tested with this type of question, but the answers do not require expansion.

(3) Outline **two** causes of desertification at the edge of some hot deserts. (2 marks, ★)

Cause 1: ....

....

Cause 2: ....

....

(4) Suggest how people may be able to slow or prevent the process of desertification. (4 marks, ★)

....

....

....

....

....

....

....

....

Study **Figure 6**, a photograph of a hot desert ecosystem.

Figure 6

NAIL IT!

Photographs are a useful source of geographical information. Sometimes you may have to look for specific pieces of information in order to answer a question, and sometimes the image may be used as a reminder of what you have learned to help you answer a question (such as **Figure 6** on the left, and Question 5, below).

(5) Using **Figure 6**, explain why a hot desert ecosystem is considered vulnerable. (4 marks, ★★★)

....

....

....

....

....

....

....

....

6 Describe and explain the importance of links within a hot desert ecosystem. (6 marks, ★★★★★)

7 For a hot desert environment you have studied, to what extent are the development opportunities for people greater than the development challenges? (9 marks + 3 SPaG marks, ★★★★★)

Use a separate sheet of paper to write your answer to this question. State your chosen environment at the start of your answer.

WORKIT!

For a hot desert environment you have studied, to what extent are the biodiversity issues a result of human or natural pressures? (9 marks + 3 SPaG marks ★★★★★)

How to tackle this question:

- In this question, you will need to include an accurate description, some explanation and a judgement on the relative importance of human and natural pressures.
- Avoid writing lengthy definitions of biodiversity and the pressures – these can be explained in your sentences that answer the question 'to what extent'.

Key ideas to include in an answer to this question:

- The possible changes to biodiversity such as loss of species (plants and animals), extinction of species, changes to habitats and lack of adaptation time.
- Natural pressures, which include the variability in temperature and precipitation.
- For hot deserts, consider the low precipitation (daily and annually) and the high daytime and low night-time temperatures.
- Human pressures include exploitation of resources such as oil, increased population numbers in relatively small areas, modern lifestyle compared to traditional lifestyle, and climate change (enhanced global warming).
- Statements that link biodiversity issues to natural pressures.
- Summary sentences or a conclusion that make a judgement on whether:
  - i human pressures are more responsible for biodiversity issues and by how much, or
  - ii natural pressures are more responsible for biodiversity issues and by how much, or
  - iii human and natural pressures are equally responsible for biodiversity issues.

Cold environments

Answer **either** questions on Hot desert environments **or** questions on Cold environments.

Study **Figure 7**, which shows a climate graph for a cold environment.

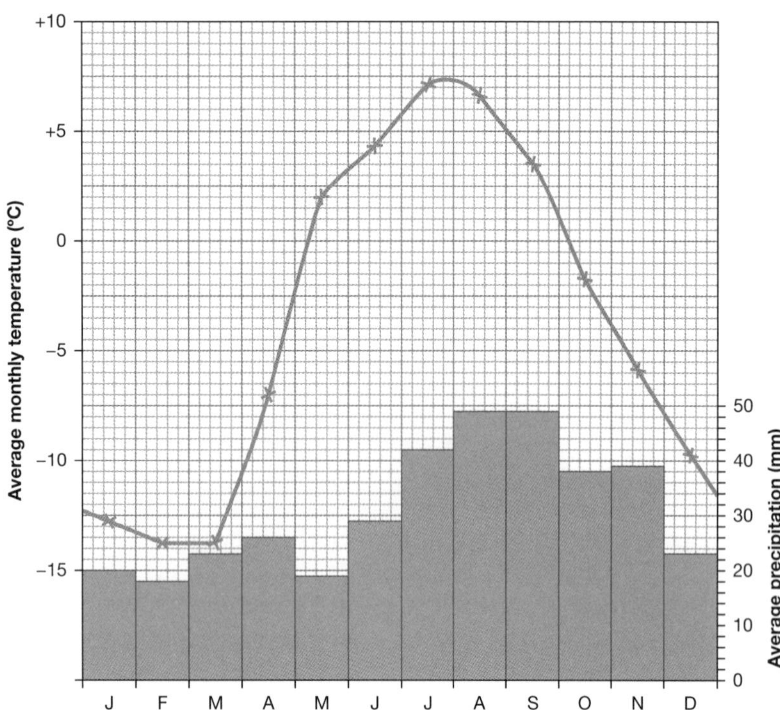

Figure 7

You will have studied *either* Hot desert environments or Cold environments. In the exam do not answer questions on both!

1. Using **Figure 7**, which one of the following temperatures is the correct average monthly temperature for December?

   Shade **one** circle only. (1 mark, ★)

   A +7.1°C ◯

   B −1.7°C ◯

   C −5.9°C ◯

   D −9.9°C ◯

NAILIT!

Don't forget: in questions that require you to write a number as an answer, you should **always give the units** for a complete answer. For example, rainfall (or precipitation) is measured in millimetres (mm).

2. Using **Figure 7**, state the average total rainfall for January. (1 mark, ★)

   ....

3. Outline how plants and/or animals have adapted to survive in cold environments. (2 marks, ★)

   ....

   ....

   ....

   ....

   ....

   ....

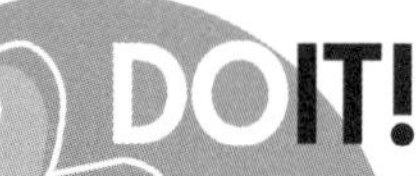

Outline

The command word *outline* means that in your answer you must state the main characteristics of something. There is a wide range of geographical factors and processes that could be tested with this type of question, but the answers do not require expansion.

Study **Figure 8,** which shows a cold environment ecosystem.

Figure 8

4 Explain why a cold environment ecosystem is considered vulnerable. (4 marks, ★★★)

5 Suggest how cold environment wilderness areas can be useful to people. (2 marks, ★)

6 Describe and explain how problems arising from economic development in cold environments can be reduced. (6 marks, ★★★★★)

....

....

....

....

7 For a cold environment you have studied, to what extent are the characteristics of the ecosystem a result of the climatic conditions?

Use a separate sheet of paper to write your answer to this question. State your chosen environment at the start of your answer. (9 marks + 3 SPaG marks, ★★★★★)

WORKIT!

For a cold environment you have studied, to what extent are the biodiversity issues a result of human or natural pressures? (9 marks + 3 SPaG marks ★★★★★)

How to tackle this question:

- In this question, you will need to include an accurate description, some explanation and a judgement on the relative importance of human and natural pressures.
- Avoid writing lengthy definitions of biodiversity and the pressures – these can be explained in your sentences that answer the question 'to what extent'.

Key ideas to include in an answer to this question:

- The possible changes to biodiversity such as loss of species (plants and animals), extinction of species, changes to habitats and lack of adaptation time.
- Natural pressures, which include variability in temperature and precipitation.
- For cold environments, consider wind chill, the low precipitation (daily and annually), and the very low winter temperatures and short summer.
- Human pressures include exploitation of resources such as oil, increased population numbers in relatively small areas, modern lifestyle compared to traditional lifestyle, and climate change (enhanced global warming).
- Statements that link biodiversity issues to natural pressures.
- Summary sentences or a conclusion that make a judgement on whether:
  - i human pressures are more responsible for biodiversity issues and by how much, or
  - ii natural pressures are more responsible for biodiversity issues and by how much, or
  - iii human and natural pressures are equally responsible for biodiversity issues.

Physical landscapes in the UK
Coastal landscapes in the UK

Answer **two** questions from the following:

questions on Coasts, questions on Rivers, questions on Glacial landscapes.

Shade the circles below to indicate which **two** optional questions you will answer.

Coasts ◯ Rivers ◯ Glacial ◯

You will have studied *two* topics from Coasts, Rivers and Glacial landscapes. The exam paper will be divided into sections on those three subjects. In the exam, only answer questions on **two** of these topics.

Study **Figure 1**, a 1: 50 000 Ordnance Survey map extract of part of the area around Hurst Castle in Hampshire.

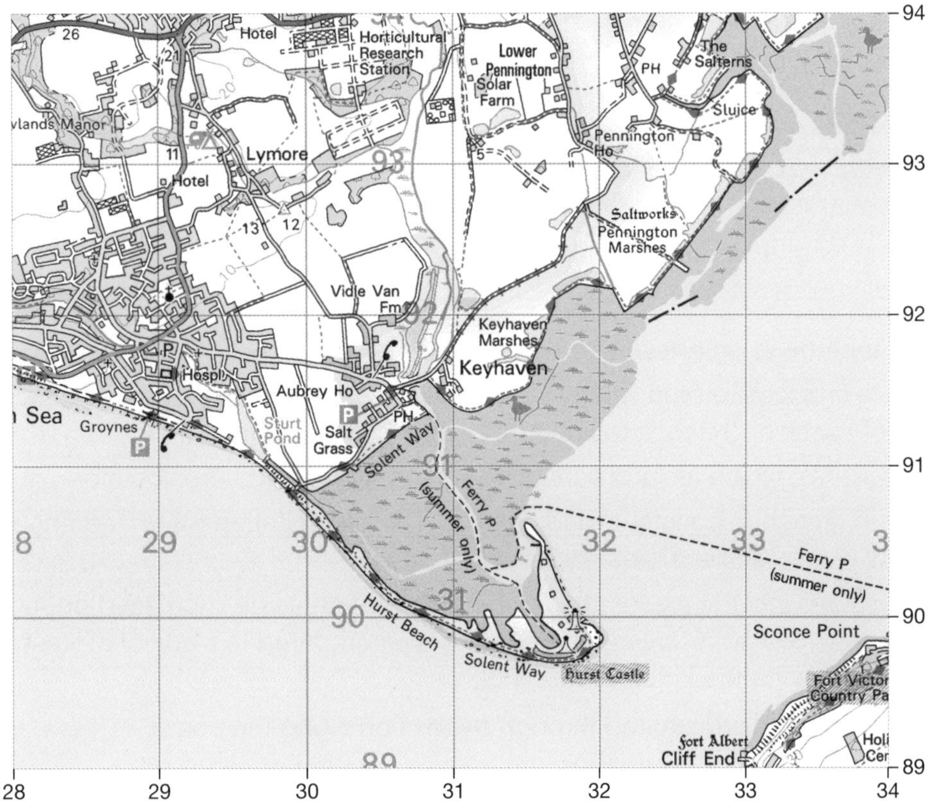

Figure 1

1. Identify the landform shown in grid squares 3090, 3189 and 3190 in **Figure 1**. (1 mark, ★)

....

2. Name the process that was involved in creating the landform shown in **Figure 1**. (1 mark, ★)

....

3. Using **Figure 1**, identify the grid reference for Hurst Castle.

   Shade **one** circle only. (1 mark, ★)

   A 898318 ◯

   B 318897 ◯

   C 908318 ◯

   D 318908 ◯

Learn how to read four- and six-figure grid references. A good way of remembering grid references is to always read from the bottom left-hand corner of the map extract and read '*along the corridor and up the stairs*'. (Read horizontal figures followed by vertical figures.)

4 Explain the difference between constructive and destructive waves. (4 marks, ★★★)

DO IT!

Learn how coastal landforms are created by erosion or deposition. A good way of remembering is by drawing annotated sketches to explain the processes involved in the formation of the landforms. You can also use annotated diagrams to support your answers in the exam. *Annotated* means you label the diagram in detail.

5 Explain the processes involved in the formation of an arch. (4 marks, ★★★)

6 Explain how landforms are created through deposition along the coast. (6 marks, ★★★★★)

WORKIT!

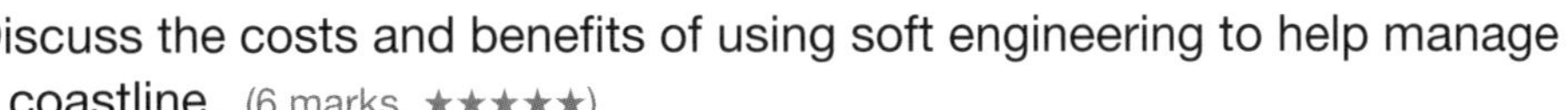

Discuss the costs and benefits of using soft engineering to help manage a coastline. (6 marks, ★★★★★)

A 'discuss' question requires you to present **key points** about an idea. You need to offer both advantages and disadvantages in your answer.

How to tackle this 'discuss' question:

Step 1 Give two benefits of soft engineering.

Step 2 Extend your points by explaining how they help to manage a coastline.

Step 3 Try to include a named example or case study to support your point, for example, management strategies used at Wallasea Island, Essex.

Step 4 Repeat steps 1–3 for costs (disadvantages, as well as actual costs) of soft engineering.

Step 5 Draw a conclusion as to whether you think soft engineering is effective in managing a coastline.

River landscapes in the UK

Study **Figure 2**, which shows a storm hydrograph.

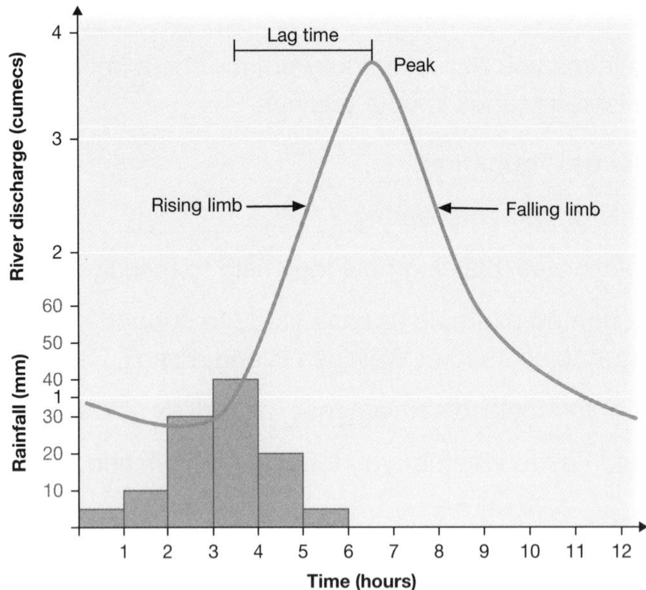

Figure 2

(1) **a** Give a definition of lag time on a hydrograph. (1 mark, ★)

....

....

b Calculate the lag time using the information in **Figure 2**. (1 mark, ★)

....

....

....

....

Don't forget that you can draw lines on graphs in the exam to help you work out answers. A ruler and sharp pencil are always useful tools for a geographer.

(2) Describe **one** physical and **one** human factor that increase the risk of flooding. (4 marks, ★★★)

....

....

....

....

....

....

....

....

Study **Figure 3**, a 1: 50 000 Ordnance Survey map extract of part of the Wye Valley, Wales.

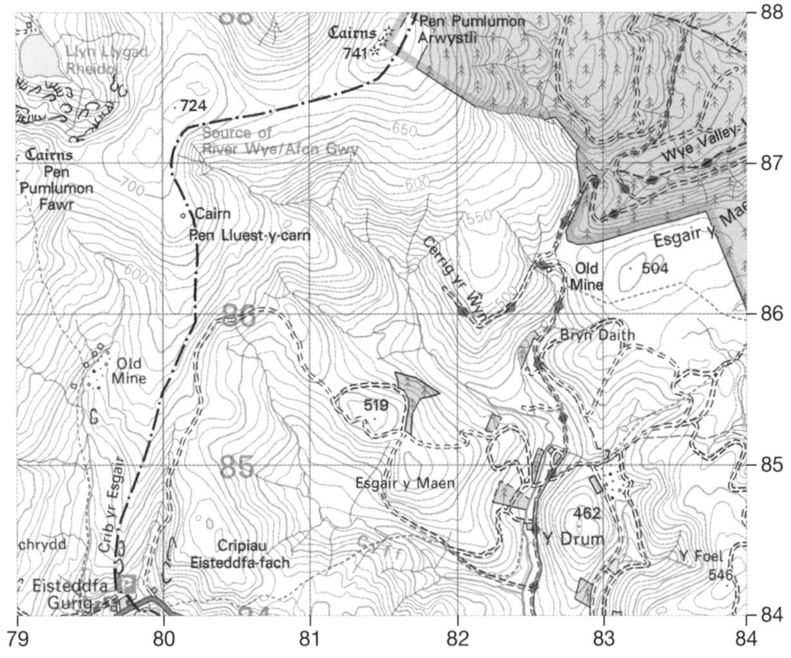

Figure 3

3. Using **Figure 3**, give **two** pieces of evidence to show that this is the upper course of a river. (4 marks, ★★)

Evidence 1: ....

....

....

Evidence 2: ....

....

....

NAILIT!

When referring to specific features on an Ordnance Survey map, it is a good idea to give a four- or six-figure grid reference to show where you have found your evidence.

4. State **two** ways in which the cross section of a river changes from source to mouth. (2 marks, ★)

1 ....

....

2 ....

....

5. Explain how the size of sediment in a river changes from source to mouth. (4 marks, ★★★)

....

....

....

....

....

....

....

Study **Figure 4**, a photograph of a river at Cuckmere Haven, East Sussex.

Figure 4

6 Using **Figure 4** and your own knowledge, explain how a floodplain is formed. (4 marks, ★★★)

....

....

....

....

....

....

....

....

NAILIT!

Make sure you learn the formation of all river landforms in four simple steps – this could be done as a flow diagram or a sequence of annotated diagrams in your revision. Include key terms and what they mean.

WORKIT!

Using a named example, assess whether hard engineering has been a success in managing floods in an area of the UK. (6 marks, ★★★★★)

An 'assess' question requires you to make an **informed judgement**. You need to offer both **advantages** and **disadvantages** in your answer.

How to tackle an 'assess' question:

Step 1 Give a definition of hard engineering.

Step 2 Give two ways in which hard engineering has been a success (think economic, social and environmental).

Step 3 Expand each point by explaining how it has helped in managing floods.

Step 4 Try to include an example to support your point, for example, the Jubilee River flood relief channel.

Step 5 Add a conclusion to say whether or not you think it has been a success.

Glacial landscapes in the UK

Study **Figure 5**, a photograph of Striding Edge in the Lake District.

Figure 5

1. Name the landform shown in **Figure 5**. (1 mark, ★)

....

NAILIT!

When labelling a diagram, make sure your arrows are clear and pointing to the exact feature.

Study **Figure 6**, a photograph of a glacier.

Figure 6

2. **a** On **Figure 6**, locate and label these features: (4 marks, ★★★)

   Lateral moraine   Terminal moraine   Meltwater   Snout

   b State another feature created by glacial erosion (not shown in **Figure 6**). (1 mark, ★)

   ....

3. Explain the formation of a drumlin. (4 marks ★★★)

DO IT!

A diagram would be useful for answering this question. Use your own paper to create one. Make sure you use an arrow to indicate the direction of ice flow.

4. Describe how economic activities have developed in glaciated upland areas. (4 marks, ★★★)

NAIL IT!

A four-mark question is always point marked. This means that you need to give two points and develop them. You should include a named example or case study.

WORK IT!

Using a named example, assess whether tourism has been a success in a UK glaciated upland area. (6 marks, ★★★★★)

An 'assess' question requires you to make an **informed judgement**. You need to offer both **advantages** and **disadvantages** in your answer.

How to tackle this 'assess' question:

Step 1 Give two ways in which tourism has been a success (think economic, social and environmental).

Step 2 Extend each point by explaining how it has helped tourism to be successful.

Step 3 Try to include an example to support your point, for example, tourism in the Lake District.

Step 4 Repeat steps 1–3 for the problems created by tourism.

Step 5 Add a conclusion to say whether or not you think it has been a success.

Urban issues and challenges
Global patterns of urban change

Study **Figure 1**, a graph showing world population growth from 1800 to 2050 (predicted).

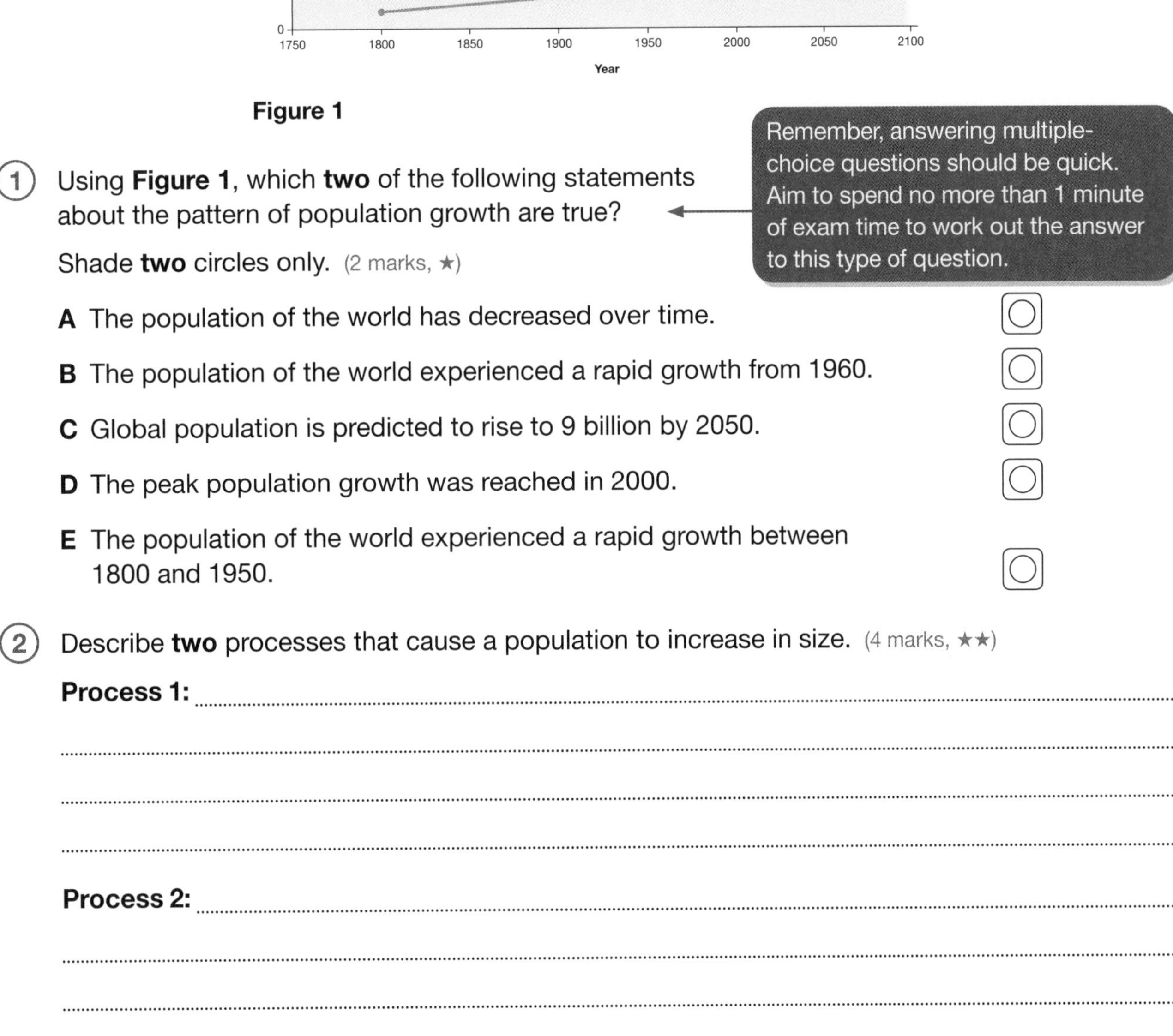

Figure 1

Remember, answering multiple-choice questions should be quick. Aim to spend no more than 1 minute of exam time to work out the answer to this type of question.

1. Using **Figure 1**, which **two** of the following statements about the pattern of population growth are true?

   Shade **two** circles only. (2 marks, ★)

   A The population of the world has decreased over time. ◯

   B The population of the world experienced a rapid growth from 1960. ◯

   C Global population is predicted to rise to 9 billion by 2050. ◯

   D The peak population growth was reached in 2000. ◯

   E The population of the world experienced a rapid growth between 1800 and 1950. ◯

2. Describe **two** processes that cause a population to increase in size. (4 marks, ★★)

   Process 1: ....

   ....

   ....

   ....

   Process 2: ....

   ....

   ....

   ....

Study **Figure 2**, a map showing the world's megacities in 2005.

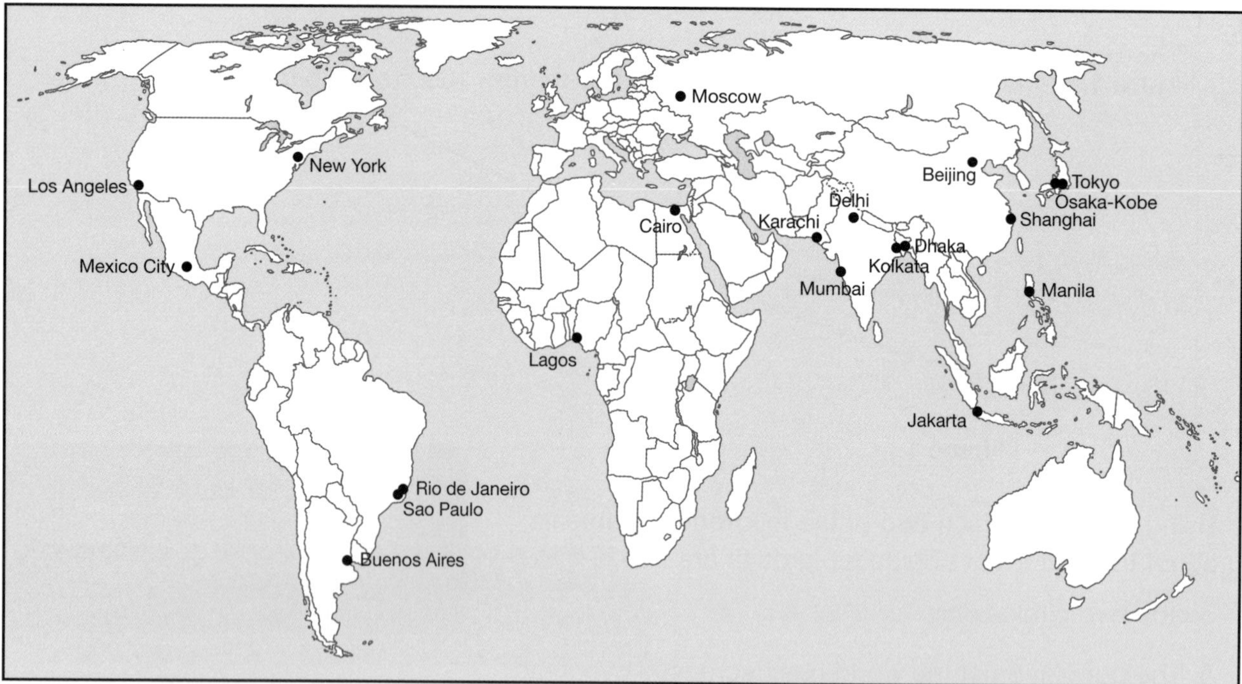

Figure 2

(3) Using **Figure 2**, describe the distribution of the world's largest cities (in 2005). (2 marks, ★)

....

....

....

....

NAILIT!

Describe the distribution

The command phrase in this two-mark question is *describe the distribution*. In your answer, you need to say where the largest cities in the world are.

- Are there more in the northern hemisphere or southern hemisphere?
- Are there more megacities in Asia or elsewhere?
- Are there any continents where there are no megacities?

Study **Figure 3**, a graph showing the urban and rural populations of the world, 1950–2050.

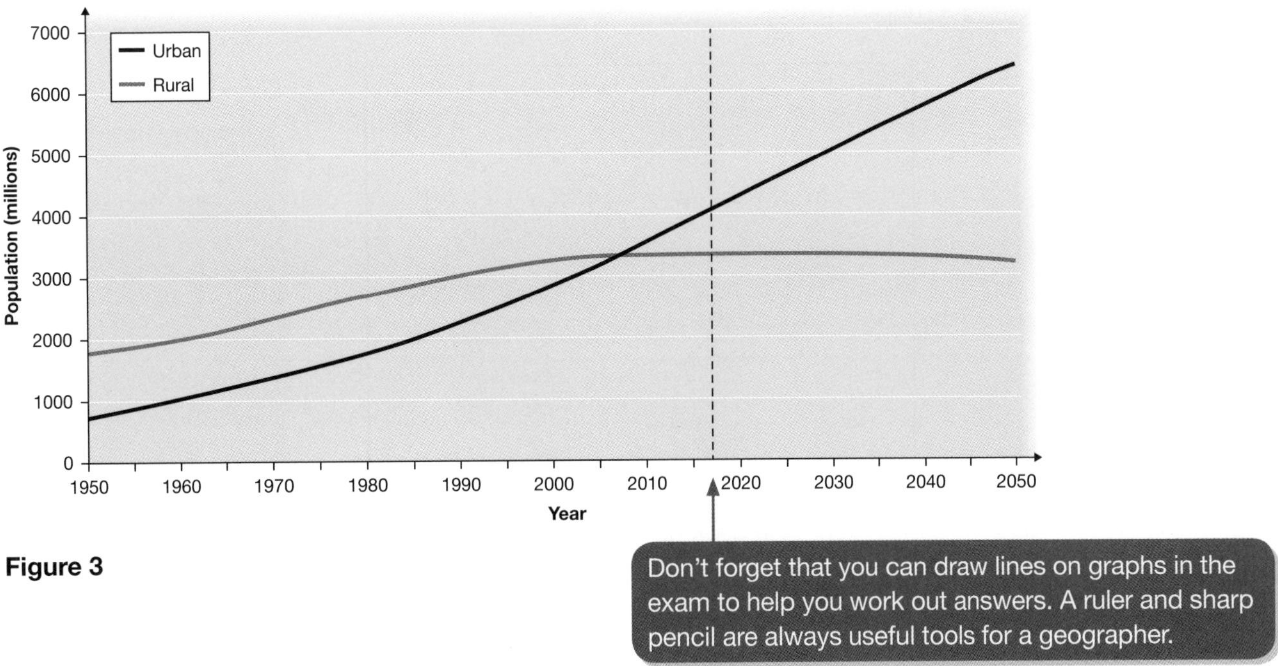

Figure 3

Don't forget that you can draw lines on graphs in the exam to help you work out answers. A ruler and sharp pencil are always useful tools for a geographer.

4. Using **Figure 3**, calculate the predicted increase in the urban population from 1950 to 2050. (1 mark, ★)

....

....

5. Explain why there has been a global increase in urban population and a decline in rural population. (6 marks, ★★★)

....

....

....

....

....

....

....

....

....

....

....

....

Urban growth in LICs and NEEs

Study **Figure 4**, showing a map of Brazil.

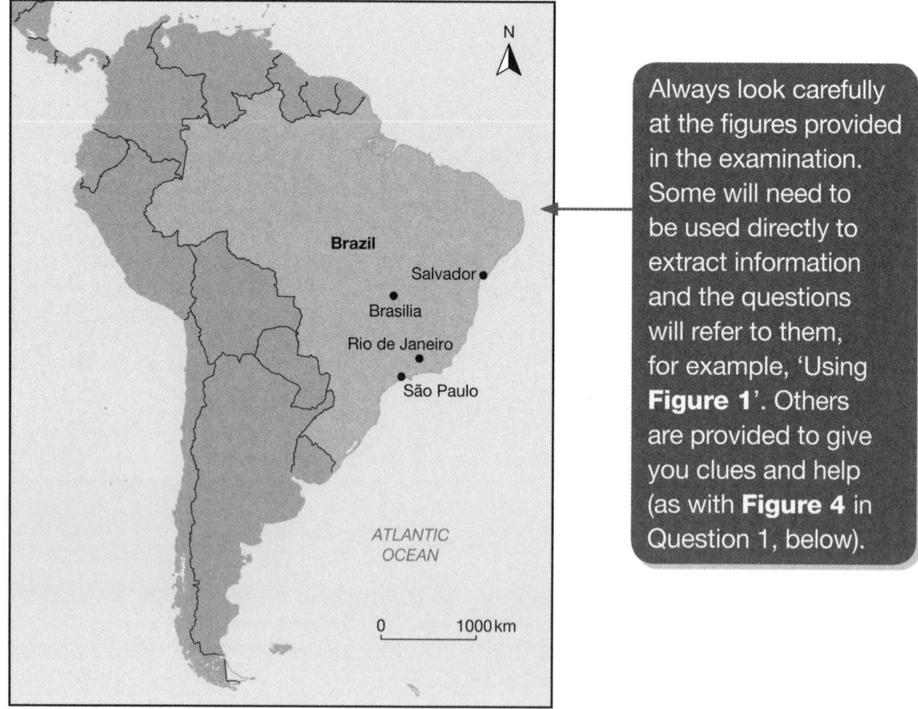

Always look carefully at the figures provided in the examination. Some will need to be used directly to extract information and the questions will refer to them, for example, 'Using **Figure 1**'. Others are provided to give you clues and help (as with **Figure 4** in Question 1, below).

Figure 4

1. Give **two** advantages of Rio de Janeiro's location as a global city. (4 marks, ★★)

Advantage 1: ....

....

....

....

Advantage 2: ....

....

....

....

2. Explain the problems of working in the informal economy for the people of LIC or NEE cities. (4 marks, ★★)

....

....

....

....

....

....

....

....

Study **Figure 5**, a photograph showing a squatter settlement.

Figure 5

3 Label the photograph to show the main problems of living in a squatter settlement. (4 marks, ★★)

NAILIT!

Labelling a photograph or diagram

When annotating a photograph, each annotation should give a point and an explanation. For example:

Open sewer, which is unhygienic, may attract rats and this can spread diseases among the people.

WORKIT!

To what extent do squatter settlements in developing countries provide social and economic opportunities for people? (6 marks, ★★★)

This 'to what extent' question is asking how much you agree or disagree with an idea. This means you need to include points **both for** and **against** the idea.

How to tackle this 'to what extent' question:

Step 1 Give **two** social and economic opportunities created by squatter settlements.

Step 2 Extend your points by explaining how they create opportunities.

Step 3 Always include an example to support your point, for example, favelas in Rio de Janeiro.

Step 4 Offer an alternative view or counterargument, for example, why squatter settlements present social and economic challenges for people.

Step 5 Link back to the question as a final summary – do you agree or disagree with the idea that squatter settlements provide social and economic opportunities for people?

Study **Figure 6**, a graph showing methods of transport in Rio de Janeiro.

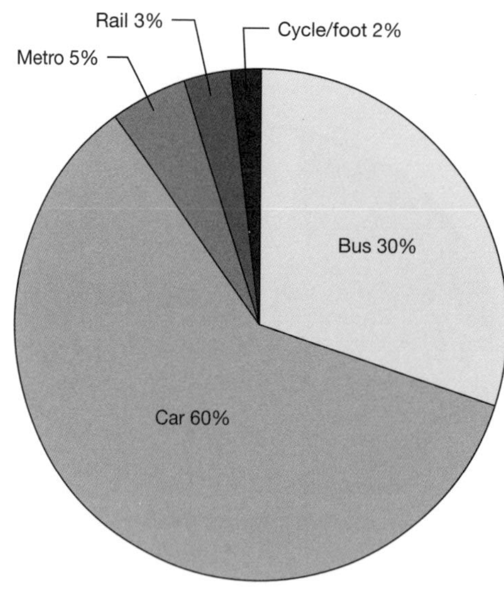

Figure 6

(4) Which transport method is most frequently used in Rio de Janeiro? (1 mark, ★)

....

(5) Describe **two** problems caused by the use of transport in an NEE city like Rio de Janeiro. (4 marks, ★★)

Problem 1: ....

....

....

....

Problem 2: ....

....

....

....

WORKIT!

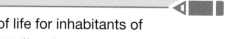

Evaluate the success of a scheme to improve the quality of life for inhabitants of squatter settlements. Use a named example in your answer. (6 marks, ★★★)

This 'evaluate' question is asking you to say how successful a scheme was in helping to improve the lives of people who live in the squatter settlements.

How to tackle this 'evaluate' question:

Step 1 Give a named example of a scheme, for example, a self-help scheme. It is also useful to include a place where it has been used, such as in the favelas of Rio de Janeiro.

Step 2 Give **two or three** ways in which the scheme works and helps to improve people's lives.

Step 3 Give **two** ways that it hasn't helped people, or state the limitations of the scheme.

Step 4 Give a final overview as a concluding sentence – do you think the successes outweigh the problems?

Urban change in the UK

Study **Figure 7**, a chart showing London's ethnic mix.

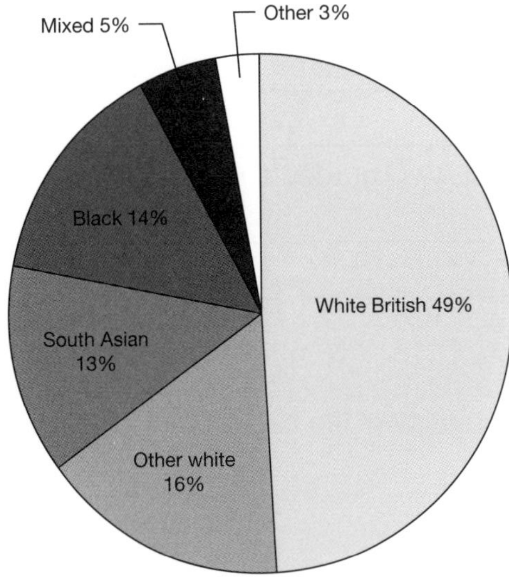

Figure 7

(1) Describe London's ethnic mix as shown in **Figure 7**. (2 marks, ★)

....

....

....

....

NAILIT!

When describing a graph or chart, you should always give the general pattern at the start of your answer and then give data or figures from the graph/chart.

(2) Give **two** reasons why cultural diversity has benefited UK cities. (4 marks, ★★)

Reason 1: ....

....

....

....

....

Reason 2: ....

....

....

....

....

Study **Figure 8**, a table showing the quality of life data for two London boroughs in 2015.

	Richmond upon Thames	Newham
Life expectancy	83 years	77 years
Unemployment	3.8%	8.5%
Pupils achieving 5 A*–C grades at GCSE	70%	57%
Average household income	£46 000	£28 000

Figure 8

③ Using **Figure 8**, compare the quality of life between the two boroughs. (4 marks, ★★)

....

....

....

....

....

....

....

....

Study **Figure 9**, a photograph of the Queen Elizabeth Park at the Olympic Park in Stratford.

Figure 9

NAILIT!

Photographs are a useful source of geographical information. Sometimes you may have to look for specific pieces of information in order to answer a question, and sometimes the image may be used as a reminder of what you have learned to help you answer a question (such as **Figure 9** and Question 4, opposite).

4 Using **Figure 9** and an example you have studied, describe how the environment was improved as part of a regeneration project. (4 marks, ★★)

....

....

....

....

....

....

....

....

WORKIT!

Evaluate the effectiveness of an urban regeneration project you have studied. (9 marks + 3 SPaG marks, ★★★★★)

'Evaluate' questions want to know how successful a scheme was, so you need to include points **both for** and **against** the scheme. You could also consider the economic, social and environmental costs and benefits.

SPaG marks give extra marks for your spelling, punctuation and grammar.

How to tackle this 'evaluate' question:

Step 1 Give **three** social, economic and environmental benefits of the scheme.

Step 2 Extend your points by **explaining** the social, economic and environmental benefits.

Step 3 Always include an example to support your points, for example, Newham and the Olympic Park.

Step 4 Repeat steps 1–3, this time giving **three** costs of the scheme (use social, economic and environmental).

Step 5 Give a final conclusion that summarises whether or not the scheme has been a success.

This is a longer written answer and not necessarily straightforward. It may be advisable to make a brief plan for your answer in any available space on the exam paper, to help you link a sequence of points in a fluent way.

NAILIT!

Spelling, punctuation and grammar (SPaG) marks

In the longer answer questions, you will be assessed on your ability to present a fluent answer using correct spelling and punctuation, good-quality grammar (such as sentence structure) and geographical terms. Make sure that you have prepared for this. Sometimes it can make a difference of a grade!

Urban sustainability in the UK

1 Which of the following is a correct definition for 'urban sustainability'?

Shade **one** circle only. (1 mark, ★)

A Rural areas organised without an over-reliance on urban areas nearby. ◯

B The need for urban areas to consume as much energy and resources as they need to function. ◯

C Cities organised without an over-reliance on the rural area surrounding them, and using renewable energy. ◯

D Urban and rural areas both consume energy and resources to provide for the population living there. ◯

NAILIT!

Multiple-choice questions

While multiple-choice questions are generally regarded as easier questions, it is important not to rush them and make silly mistakes. Look at each option (A, B, C and D) carefully and consider its meaning. You could put a cross over the wording of the incorrect answers as you rule them out – but never put any mark over the circle at the end of the option. Only shade the circle of the answer you have worked out is correct.

2 Identify **two** factors that contribute to a city's ecological footprint. (2 marks, ★)

Factor 1: ....

....

Factor 2: ....

....

3 Describe **two** features of a sustainable urban community. (4 marks, ★ ★)

Feature 1: ....

....

....

....

....

Feature 2: ....

....

....

....

....

....

NAILIT!

A four-mark question is always point marked. This means you need to give two points and develop them.

Study **Figure 10**, a photograph showing a cyclist using the Cycle Superhighway in central London.

Figure 10

4 Explain how cycling can be an important part of a sustainable transport strategy. (4 marks, ★★)

....

....

....

....

....

....

....

....

NAILIT!

Make sure you learn your named examples or case studies so that you can provide specific examples to support your answers.

5 For a named city you have studied, evaluate the strategies employed to manage traffic congestion. (6 marks, ★★★)

....

....

....

....

....

....

....

....

6 Give **two** advantages of developing areas of green space in urban areas. (4 marks, ★★)

Advantage 1: ....

....

....

....

Advantage 2: ....

....

....

....

WORKIT!

Suggest ways that cities can be more sustainable. (6 marks, ★★★)

A 'suggest' question requires you to present a possible case for something, in this case, how cities could be made more sustainable.

Step 1 Give **three** ways in which cities can become more sustainable (think social and environmental).

Step 2 Extend your points by explaining how these suggestions are sustainable.

Step 3 Always include an example to support your points, for example, East Village in London.

Step 4 Add a conclusion to say whether or not you think it is possible for cities to be sustainable.

The changing economic world
Economic development and quality of life

Study **Figure 1**, part of a world map showing a classification of countries using average income per person (capita).

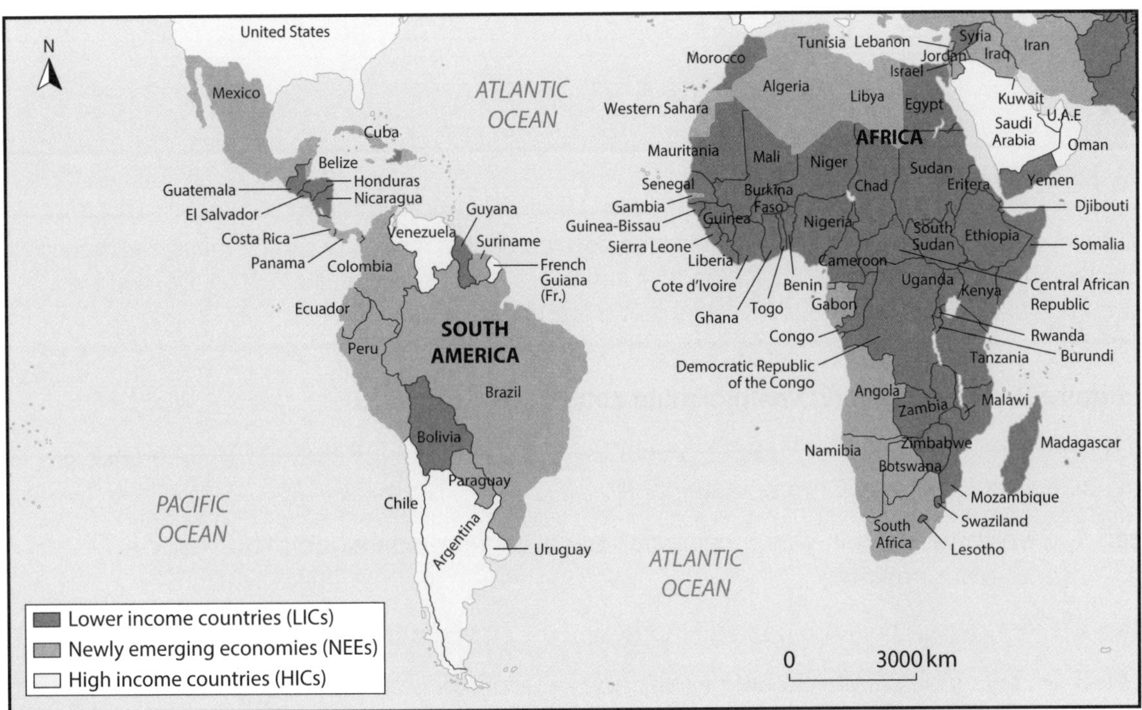

Figure 1

DO IT!

Using keys

Make sure that you always use the keys to maps carefully. In **Figure 1**, for example, in which category is Argentina? In which category is Chad? In which category are Bolivia and Zambia?

1. Using **Figure 1**, compare the classification of countries in South America with those in Africa. (2 marks, ★)

....

....

....

....

'Compare' in this question means look for **similarities** and **differences** in the classification categories between South America and Africa. You don't need to count the number of countries in each category. Instead, for example, look for the most common categories, or missing categories.

2. **Figure 1** shows a classification of countries according to income. Outline **one** advantage of using average income per person to measure the development of a country. (2 marks, ★★★)

....

....

....

....

③ Outline **one** disadvantage of the Human Development Index (HDI) as a measure of a country's development. (2 marks, ★★★)

....

....

....

....

NAILIT!

You need to learn the different ways in which the development of a country can be measured, especially gross national income (GNI) per capita (person) and the Human Development Index (HDI), and the strengths and weaknesses of each development measure.

Study **Figure 2**, a map showing world climate zones.

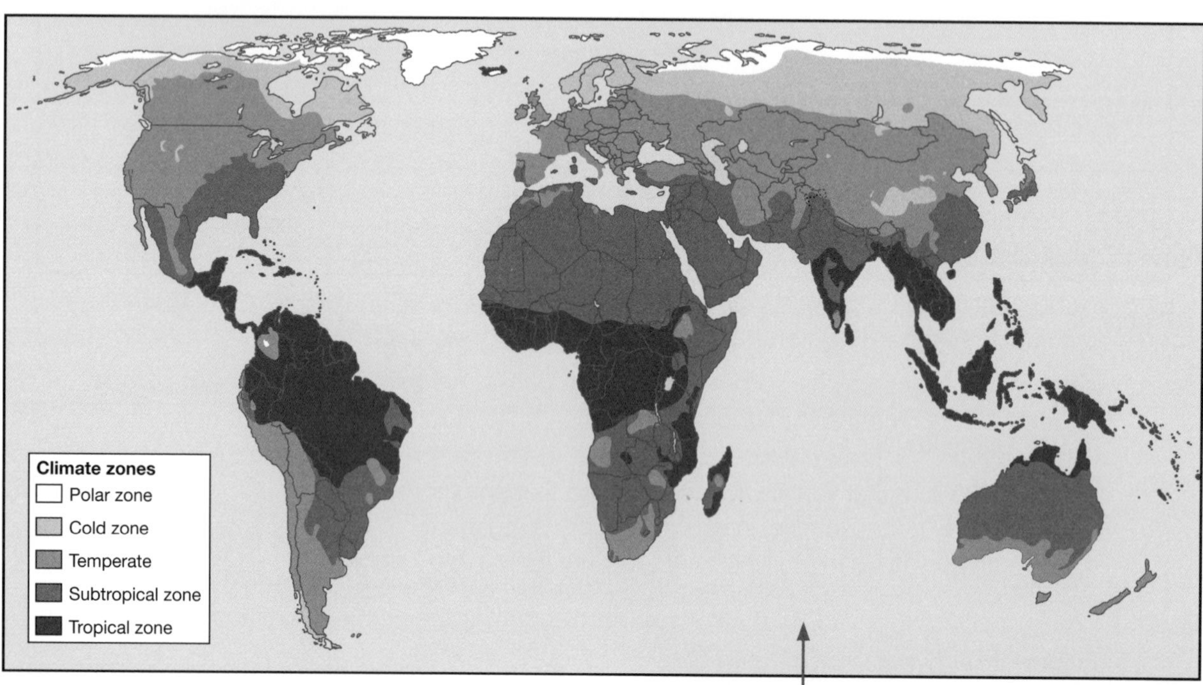

Figure 2

Always look carefully at the figures provided in the exam. Some will need to be used directly to extract information and the questions will usually refer to them, for example, 'Using **Figure 1**' (in Question 1) Others are provided to give you clues and help (as with **Figure 2** in Question 4).

④ Explain how **one** aspect of physical geography and climate may cause uneven development between countries. (4 marks, ★★★)

....

....

....

....

....

....

....

....

WORKIT!

Study **Figure 3**, a graph showing the share of world exports (goods) (2005 and 2014) for world regions.

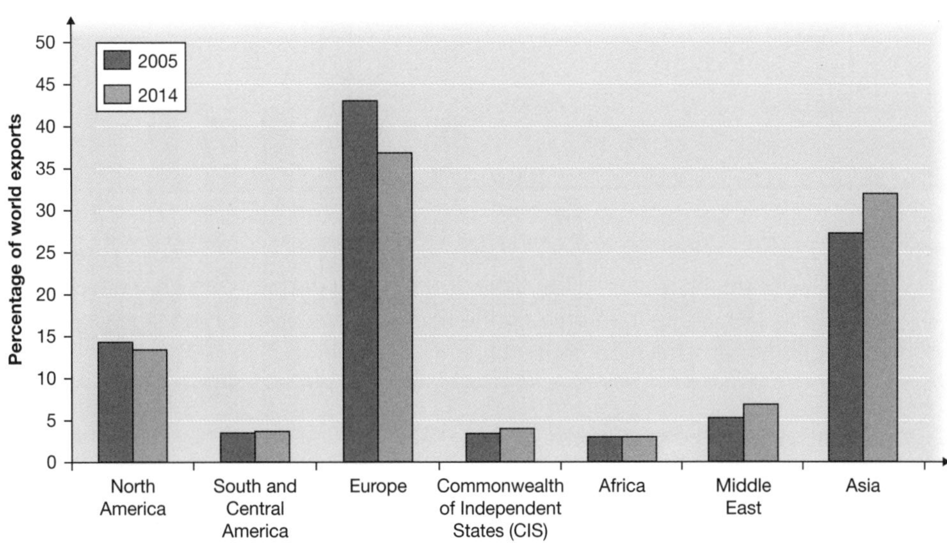

Figure 3

Explain how **one** aspect of economic geography may cause uneven development between countries. (4 marks, ★★★)

How to tackle this question:

The following steps will help you to produce a good standard of answer to this question. You should also study **Figure 3**, which has been included for information.

Step 1 Identify and highlight the command word or phrase. In this case '**explain** how **one aspect**', which means that you must choose one factor linked to economic geography and give reasons for it causing more development in one country than in another.

Step 2 Identify and circle the key ideas in the question. In this case, 'economic geography' and 'uneven development'. Economic geography is to do with making money and uneven development means that some countries get richer while others remain relatively poor.

Step 3 Think of one aspect of economic geography that you have studied in this topic. **Figure 3** has been included to give you a massive clue: **trade**, you could choose the lack of Foreign Direct Investment (FDI), the lack of spending on services such as education and health, or government policies or corruption.

Step 4 In your answer, show how your chosen aspect of economic geography (for example, trade) creates 'richer' countries (HICs and NEEs) and 'poorer' countries (LICs), with two or three well-developed sentences that identify the geographical links.

DOIT!

Give **two** reasons why the suggested Stage 5 of the demographic transition model may be characterised by an ageing population. (2 marks, ★★★)

When asked for two reasons, make sure that they are different and not just the same reason written in a different way!

Study the student answer below, give it a mark out of 2 and suggest how it could be improved:

Stage 5 has a lot of older people because they are living longer. People live longer because there is much better health care.

Study **Figure 4**, a graph showing the number of cases of the disease tuberculosis (per 100 000 people) in 2014 for selected countries.

Note that the graph uses a logarithmic scale.

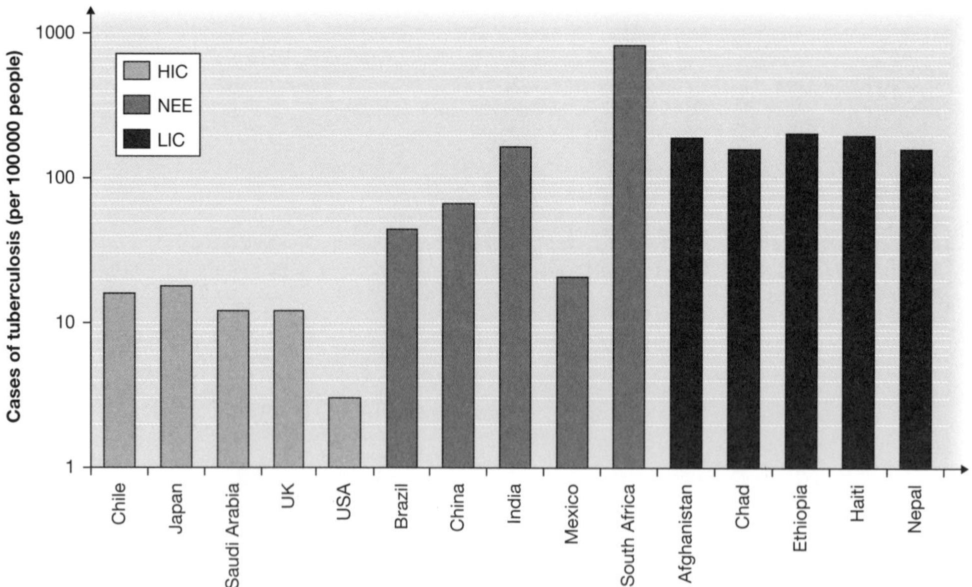

Figure 4

5. Using **Figure 4**, calculate the difference between the number of cases of tuberculosis (per 100 000 people) in Haiti and the USA. (1 mark, ★)

....

....

6. Explain why there is such a large variation in the number of cases of tuberculosis between the countries shown in **Figure 4**. (4 marks, ★★★)

....

....

....

....

....

....

....

....

NAILIT!

Sometimes graphs may have a logarithmic (log) scale on one axis (or both axes) when there is a large range in the data to be presented (i.e. very large numbers compared with very small numbers). **Figure 4** has a log scale on the vertical *y*-axis, showing the number of cases of tuberculosis per 100 000 people in a population. Even though the horizontal lines are spaced differently from a normal graph, each line still represents a unit of measurement. In this case, each line between 1 and 10 increases by 1, each line between 10 and 100 increases by 10, and each line between 100 and 1000 increases by 100. Examiners know that logarithmic graphs are tricky to interpret and will make skills questions based on them as easy as possible.

7. Suggest **two** reasons why poor health may create a cycle of poverty. (2 marks, ★★★)

Reason 1: ....

....

Reason 2: ....

....

Global development gap

Study **Figure 5**, a graph showing outflowing Foreign Direct Investment (FDI) in $ billions by world group or region 2012–14.

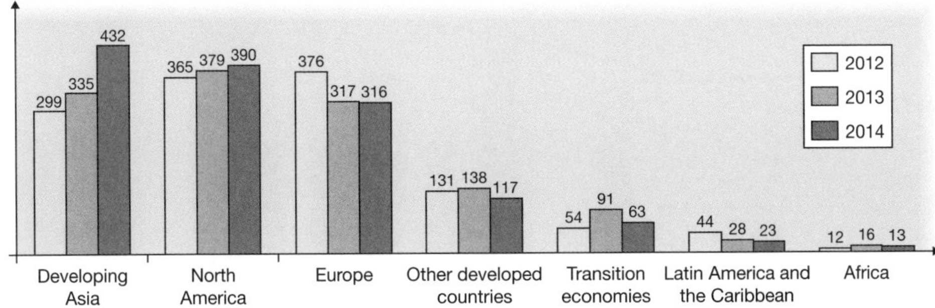

Figure 5

Sometimes there may be several possible answers to a one-mark question, but only one needs to be given. For example, in Question **1a**, change could be simply up or down, or a rate of change, or the size of the change.

1 a Using **Figure 5**, compare the change in developing Asia with the change in Europe between 2012 and 2014. (1 mark, ★)

....

....

b Calculate the difference between the amount of outflowing FDI from transition economies and the amount outflowing from Africa in 2014. (1 mark, ★)

....

....

2 Outline **one** way in which FDI can help to increase the development of a country. (2 marks, ★)

....

....

....

....

3 Suggest **one** reason why FDI is not always successful in reducing poverty within a country. (2 marks, ★★★)

....

....

....

....

NAILIT!

If you are asked for **one** reason, way or problem, and the question is worth two marks, you must provide a fully developed answer. You must explore the **geographical links** within this point in relation to the theme of the question to gain both marks.

Study **Figure 6**, a graph showing the number of tourists visiting Jamaica and the income received from them.

Tourist arrivals (millions)/income ($ billions)
4
3.5
3
2.5
2
1.5
1
0.5
0
2009 2010 2011 2012 2013 2014 2015
Years
Total tourist arrivals (millions)
Tourist money ($ billions)

Figure 6

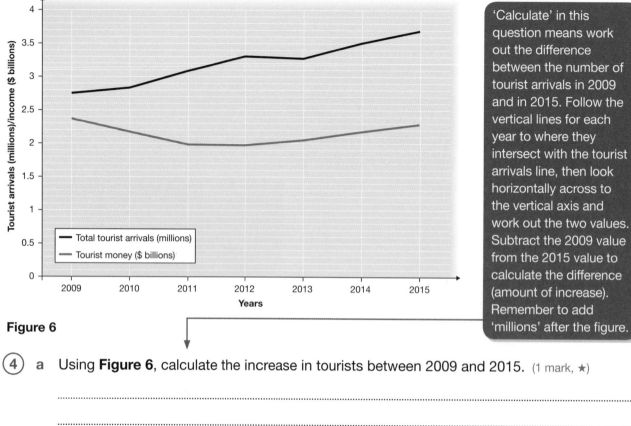

'Calculate' in this question means work out the difference between the number of tourist arrivals in 2009 and in 2015. Follow the vertical lines for each year to where they intersect with the tourist arrivals line, then look horizontally across to the vertical axis and work out the two values. Subtract the 2009 value from the 2015 value to calculate the difference (amount of increase). Remember to add 'millions' after the figure.

4 a Using **Figure 6**, calculate the increase in tourists between 2009 and 2015. (1 mark, ★)

....

....

b Using **Figure 6**, compare the trend of tourist arrivals with the trend of tourist income from 2009 to 2015. (1 mark, ★)

....

....

5 Outline **one** way in which tourism may help break the cycle of poverty in Jamaica. (2 marks, ★)

....

....

....

....

6 Suggest **one** disadvantage that tourism may bring to an LIC or NEE like Jamaica. (2 marks, ★★★)

....

....

....

....

NAILIT!

Learn all of the ways in which a country can try to develop economically and improve the quality of life for its people. Think about how successful each of these ways has been or could be in the future.

Justify

Make sure that you know what to do when instructed to 'justify' – this means that you must make a case for your decision. In Question 7, you have a choice between *yes* and *no*, and then you must fully support your answer with as much evidence as possible. There is no right or wrong decision (*yes/no*). Instead, the examiner will be looking at the **quality** of your evidence and your **use** of that evidence to support your decision.

7 'Industrial change in an LIC or NEE always brings significant improvements to the quality of life of poor people.'

Do you agree with this statement? Yes ☐ No ☐

Justify your decision.

Use a separate sheet of paper to write your answer to this question. (9 marks + 3 SPaG marks, ★★★★★)

This is a longer written answer and not necessarily straightforward. It may be advisable to make a brief plan for your answer in any available space on the exam paper, to help you link a sequence of points in a fluent way.

WORK IT!

'A tourist economy always leads to a range of development benefits for all people in an LIC or NEE.'

Do you agree with this statement? Yes ☐ No ☐

Justify your decision. (9 marks + 3 SPaG marks, ★★★★★)

How to tackle this question:

- In this question you will need to include some **accurate description**, some **explanation** and a **justification** of your agreement or disagreement with the statement about the scale of benefits to be gained from tourism.
- Avoid just listing all the benefits and problems associated with tourism or just writing everything that you can recall about tourism in the LIC or NEE you have studied. In other words – answer the question.
- Read the statement. Think about what you have learned in this topic and make a decision whether you agree or disagree with it (and shade the relevant box).

Key ideas to include in an answer to this question:

- Recall the ways in which tourism benefits **or** does not benefit all people in an LIC or NEE.
- Recall the country that you have studied where tourism has been used to try to develop the country, including a range of relevant factual material. The case study in the accompanying AQA GCSE Geography Revision Guide covers Jamaica.
- If you think *yes* and agree with the statement, then points you could make include: the range of jobs from unskilled to skilled; the money that this provides for families; the money that this brings into the economy by supporting a range of local businesses (perhaps mentioning the multiplier effect); and to the government in the form of tax money, which is used to improve infrastructure and benefits everyone.
- If you think *no* and disagree with the statement, then points you could make include: that most jobs are low paid and seasonal; income from tourism varies from year to year depending on external influences such as fashion trends and economic conditions; not everyone is able to get a job in tourism and there is a big gap in income and housing quality; and some parts of a country do not benefit at all, as tourism is concentrated in a few areas.

Rapid economic development and change

Study **Figure 7**, a graph showing oil production in Nigeria from the end of 2000 to the start of 2016.

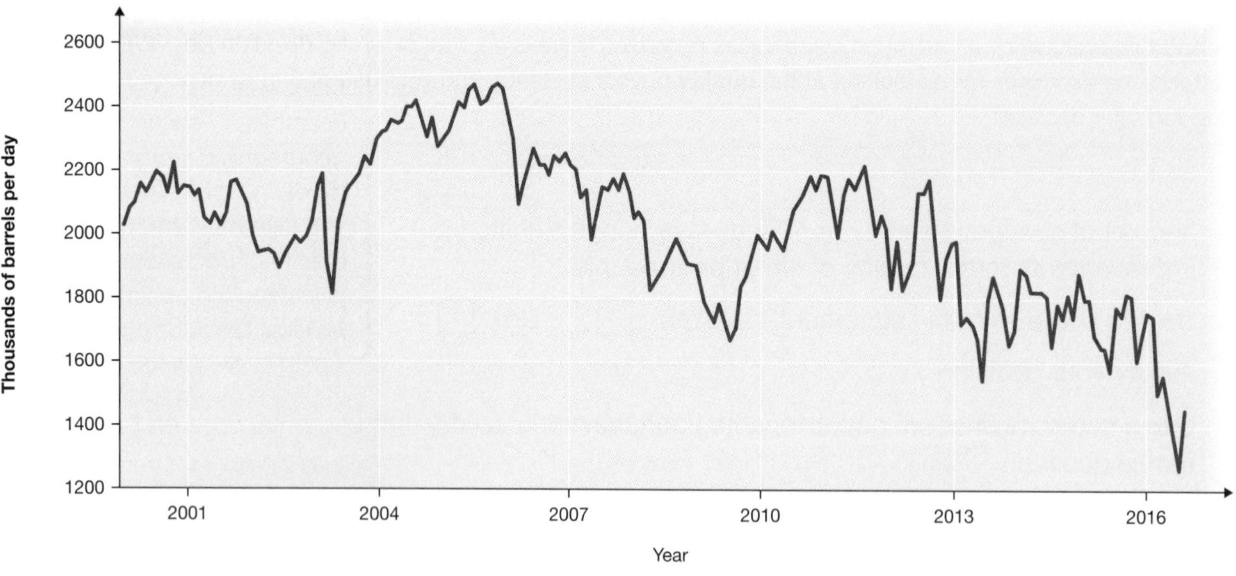

Figure 7

NAILIT!

Make sure that you can read and interpret line graphs by using the axes accurately. Sometimes you will need a ruler and sharp pencil to help work out an accurate answer by drawing lines on the graph to the axes. For example, on the graph above, from the oil production line to the vertical axis showing the amount of oil in thousands of barrels per day. Remember to always state the units of any numerical answers.

1 a Using **Figure 7**, calculate the decrease in oil production between 2004 and 2016. (1 mark, ★)

....

....

'Calculate' in this question means work out the difference between the amount of oil production in 2004 and the amount of oil production in 2016. Follow the vertical lines for each year to where they intersect with the production line, then look horizontally across to the vertical axis and work out the two production values. Subtract the 2016 value from the 2004 value to calculate the difference (amount of decrease).

b Using **Figure 7**, compare the trend of oil production between 2004 and 2007 with the trend between 2007 and 2010. (1 mark, ★)

....

....

NAILIT!

Remember that if you are asked about 'trends' then there are certain possibilities: either a downward trend (decrease), an upward trend (increase) or no change (stays about the same). However, any of these overall trends may have considerable variations within them – such as lots of 'ups' and 'downs'. There may also be no significant trend with considerable change over time, which can be called a variable trend. Make sure that you stick to the time period(s) given in the question.

(2) For an LIC or NEE country that you have studied, outline **one** political **or** social disadvantage that has restricted positive change in the country. (2 marks, ★)

....

....

....

....

....

....

....

....

NAILIT!

Political, social, cultural and environmental factors

Make sure that you remember examples of each of these geographical factors – identify two for each factor. Then make sure that you use the correct one(s) in an exam question. For example, Question 2 gives you the option of outlining **one** political factor *or* **one** social factor.

(3) Explain why the industrial structure of an LIC or NEE country that you have studied has changed. (4 marks, ★★★)

....

....

....

....

....

....

....

....

(4) 'International aid and trade are essential to the economic development of LIC or NEE countries.'

Do you agree with this statement? Yes ☐ No ☐

Justify your decision.

Use a separate sheet of paper to write your answer to this question. (9 marks + 3 SPaG marks, ★★★★★)

NAILIT!

This part of the specification tells you that you must know about a **case study of an LIC or NEE country**. In the accompanying AQA GCSE Geography Revision Guide, this is Nigeria. Make sure that you can recall specific information about Nigeria or the country that you have studied. These longer answer questions do not directly ask for a named country, but you must use your knowledge and understanding of the country you have studied to answer the question, making sure that you include some factual material that you have learned.

WORKIT!

'The quality of life for people in LIC or NEE countries is not always improved by economic development.'

Do you agree with this statement? Yes ☐ No ☐

Justify your decision. (9 marks + 3 SPaG marks, ★★★★★)

How to tackle this question:

- In this question you will need to include some **accurate description**, some **explanation** and a **justification** of your agreement or disagreement with the statement about the extent to which quality of life is improved by economic development.
- Avoid just listing all the benefits and problems associated with economic development, or writing everything that you can recall about quality of life in the LIC or NEE you have studied. In other words – answer the question.
- Read the statement. Think about what you have learned about this topic and make a decision on whether you agree or disagree with it (and shade the relevant box).

Key ideas to include in an answer to this question:

- Recall the ways in which economic development improves **or** does not improve the quality of life of people in an LIC or NEE.
- Recall the country that you have studied where there has been rapid economic development and change, including a range of relevant factual material. The accompanying AQA GCSE Geography Revision Guide case study covers Nigeria.
- If you think *yes* and agree with the statement, then points you could make include: a slow rate of improvement; low levels of spending on health care and education; poor access to sanitation; rapid population growth increasing pressures; ineffective use of money from trade and resources; civil unrest continuing; and damage to the natural environment.
- If you think *no* and disagree with the statement, then points you could make include: the improvement in quality of life as measured in different ways (such as HDI); longer life expectancy; improvements in access to fresh water and sanitation; higher enrolment in school (boys and girls); and greater income for people.

NAILIT!

Spelling, punctuation and grammar (SPaG) marks

In the longer answer questions, you will be assessed on your ability to present a fluent answer using correct spelling and punctuation, good-quality grammar (such as sentence structure) and geographical terminology. Make sure that you have prepared for this. Sometimes it can make a difference of a grade!

Changes in the UK economy

Study **Figure 8**, a graph showing the trends in employment structure (by industrial sector) in the UK from 1800 to 2000.

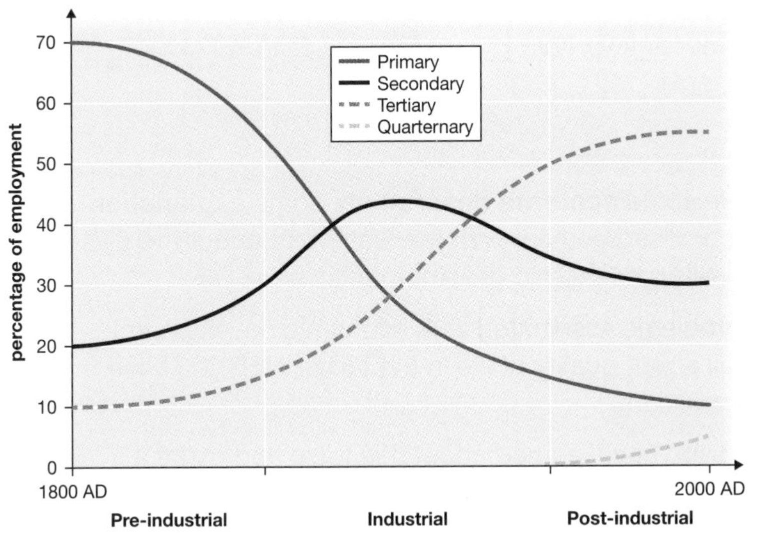

Figure 8

Make sure that you can read and interpret **multiple line graphs** accurately. Be especially careful that you use the key to identify what each line represents so that you do not muddle them up in your answers. For Question **1a**, which line is for primary and which line is for tertiary?

1 a Using **Figure 8**, compare the change in primary and tertiary employment in the UK between 1800 and 2000. (2 marks, ★)

....

....

....

....

b Give **two** reasons for the decline of secondary industry and secondary employment in the UK towards the end of the industrial stage and into the post-industrial stage (1980 to 2000). (2 marks, ★)

Reason 1: ....

....

Reason 2: ....

....

2 Explain how information technology has been creating economic opportunities in the UK since 1990. (4 marks, ★★★)

....

....

....

....

....

....

....

....

DOIT!

UK secondary sector

Make sure that you learn and remember the reasons for the decline and closure of UK manufacturing industries, such as competition from industries in NEEs. This shows up on **Figure 8** from the mid-industrial stage and continues in the post-industrial stage.

③ 'It is not possible to have economic growth in the UK without significant damage to the physical environment.'

Do you agree with this statement? Yes ☐ No ☐

Justify your decision.

Use a separate sheet of paper to write your answer to this question. (9 marks + 3 SPaG marks, ★★★★★)

These longer answer questions should be written in a fluent style, showing good use of geographical terminology. Never use lists and bullet points in longer answers.

WORKIT!

'The UK has a very significant role in the wider world.'

Do you agree with this statement? Yes ☐ No ☐

Justify your decision. (9 marks + 3 SPaG marks, ★★★★★)

How to tackle this question:

- In this question you will need to include some **accurate description**, some **explanation** and a **justification** of your agreement or disagreement with the statement.
- Avoid just listing all the ways that the UK is linked to the rest of the world. Make a judgement on how significant these links are.
- Read the statement. Think about what you have learned in this topic and make a decision on whether you agree or disagree with it (and shade the relevant box).

Key ideas to include in an answer to this question:

- Recall the ways in which the UK has an influence in the rest of the world, perhaps ranking them in order of strength of influence.
- Recall a range of relevant factual material. The accompanying AQA GCSE Geography Revision Guide has a section entitled 'The UK in the wider world'.
- If you think *yes* and agree with the statement, then points you could make include: the UK's position in the UN, NATO and the G8 meetings; the import of goods from all around the world; the colonial legacy of the English language and legal systems; the Commonwealth, immigration links, tourism links; sporting success in the Olympics; internet businesses; and provision of aid to LICs or NEEs.
- If you think *no* and disagree with the statement, then points you could make include: the decline in the UK's role since the days of the British Empire; exit from the EU; controls on immigration; the decline in manufacturing exports; lack of success in some sports; airports reaching full capacity; internet competition; and political and economic competition from NEEs.

NAILIT!

Spelling, punctuation and grammar (SPaG) marks

In the longer answer questions, you will be assessed on your ability to present a fluent answer using correct spelling and punctuation, good-quality grammar (such as sentence structure) and geographical terminology. Make sure that you have prepared for this. Sometimes it can make a difference of a grade!

The challenge of resource management
Resource management

Study **Figure 1**, showing information about world geothermal energy capacity in 2015.

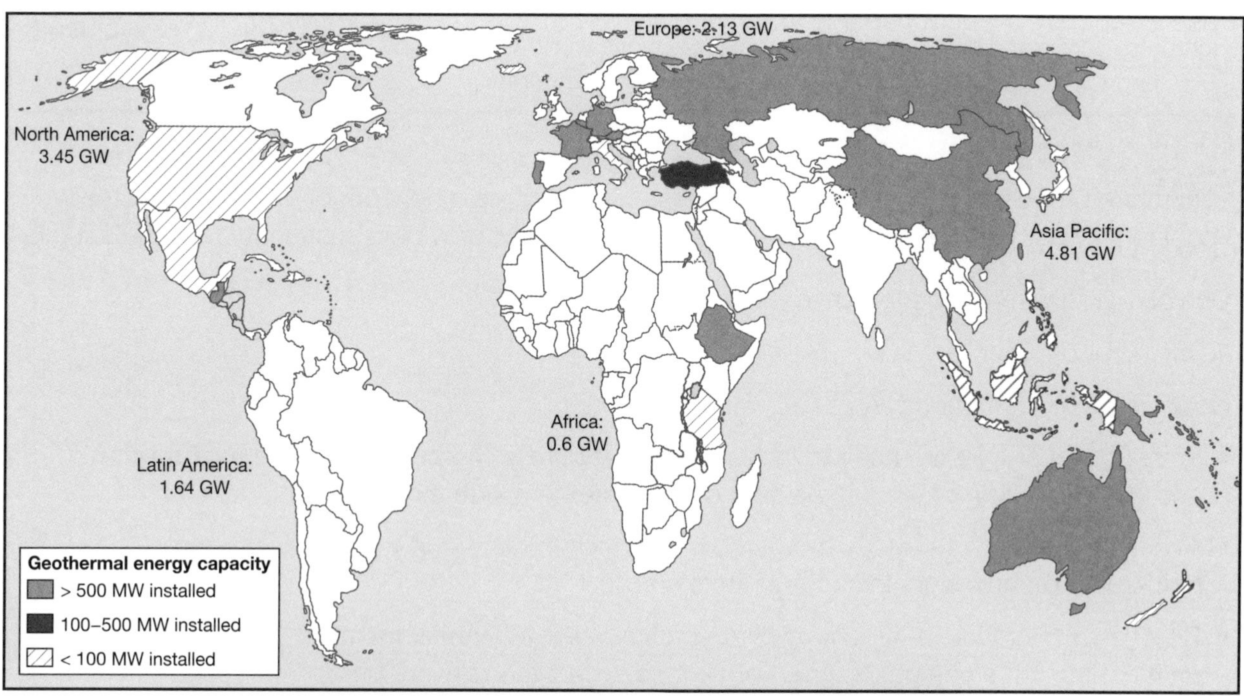

Figure 1

Make sure that you understand the meaning of the command word *suggest*. It means that there is more than one possible answer. For example, in Question 1 you have to present **one** possible reason.

1. Suggest **one** reason for the development of geothermal energy in New Zealand. (1 mark, ★)

   ....

   ....

2. Using **Figure 1**, and your geographical knowledge describe the distribution of geothermal energy capacity in the world in 2015. (2 marks, ★)

   ....

   ....

   ....

   ....

DO IT!

Location and distribution

Make sure that you understand the difference between the geographical terms 'location' and 'distribution'. *Location* is a precise position of something while *distribution* is an amount and spatial arrangement (spread) of something. For distribution, it is best to use compass directions or names of regions (if available).

Study the following student answer to Question 2; give it a mark out of 2 and suggest how it could be improved.

The areas with most geothermal capacity are found on the left of the map, and there are some scattered across the centre of the map.

NAIL IT!

Knowledge of geographical terminology, such as *sustainable* and *geothermal energy,* is very important for the exam. This helps you to understand questions, improve the quality of your answers by using correct geographical terms and gain SPaG marks in the questions worth higher marks. The accompanying AQA GCSE Geography Revision Guide contains a Glossary of such terms.

3. There are proposals to link Iceland to the rest of Europe via a network of undersea electricity cables. Explain why this is considered to be important for providing sustainable energy supplies to Europe in the future. (6 marks, ★★★)

Study **Figure 2**, a graph showing the quality of water in three UK river basins in 2012.

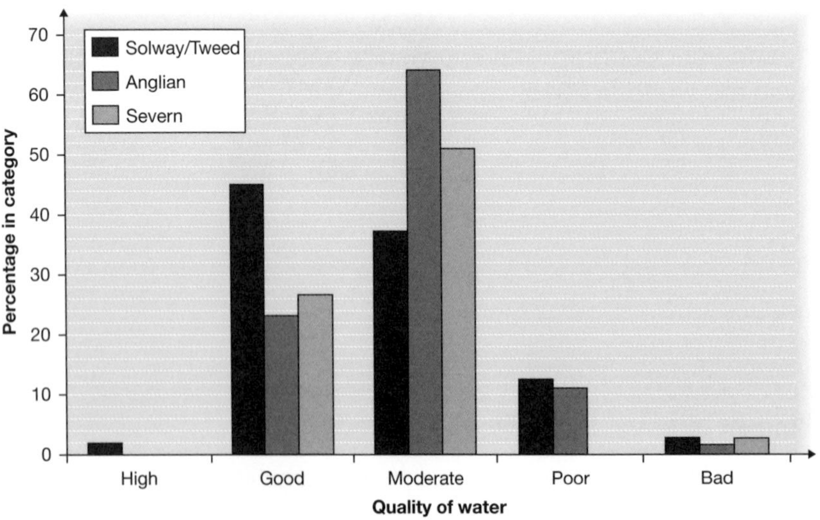

Figure 2

4. Using **Figure 2**, complete the graph for the River Severn basin using the following data. (1 mark, ★)

Poor 19.7%

⑤ Using **Figure 2**, which **one** of the following statements is correct about the water quality in the three river basins?

Shade **one** circle only. (1 mark, ★)

A The Severn has more moderate water quality than the other two river basins. ○

B The Anglian has better water quality than the other two river basins. ○

C The Solway/Tweed has the worst water quality of all three river basins. ○

D The Solway/Tweed has the best water quality of all three river basins. ○

Study **Figure 3**, a map showing a possible multi-purpose scheme, proposed in 2013.

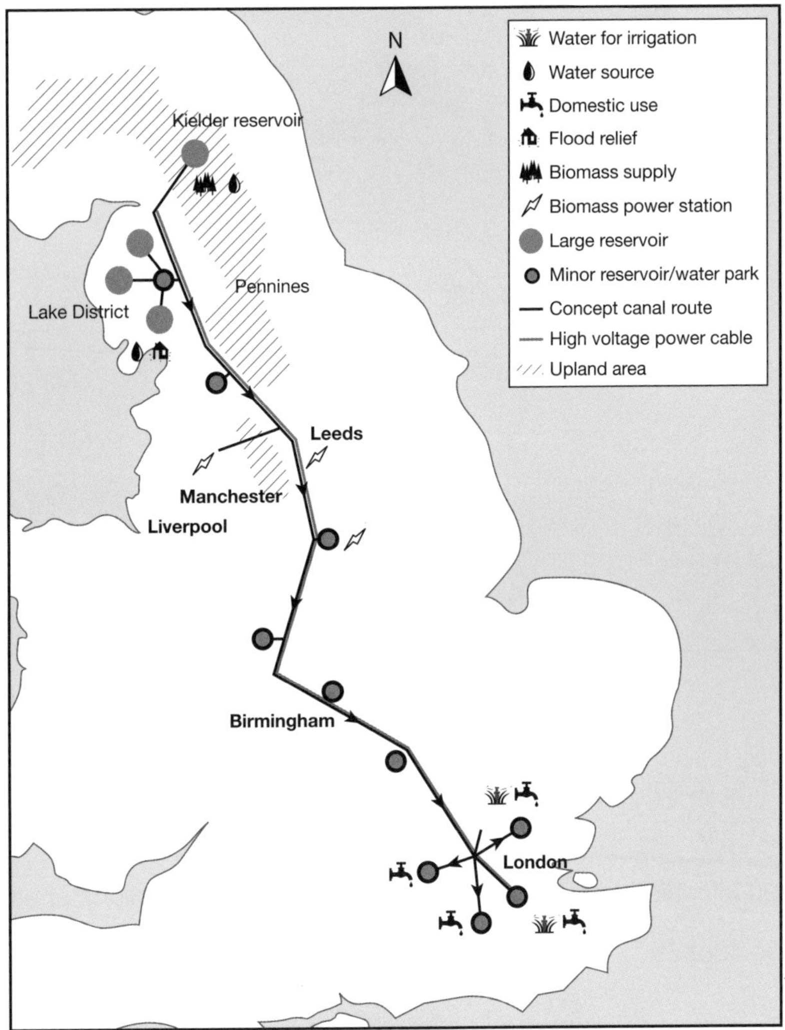

Figure 3

⑥ Using **Figure 3**, suggest why water transfer was a major part of this proposed scheme to link the North to the South-East of England. (3 marks, ★★★★★)

....

....

....

....

....

....

Food

Answer **either** questions on Food **or** questions on Water **or** questions on Energy.

You will have studied *either* Food *or* Water *or* Energy. The exam paper will be divided into sections on Food, Water and Energy. In the exam, only answer questions on **one** of these topics.

Shade the circle below to indicate which optional questions you will answer.

Shade **one** circle only

Food ◯ Water ◯ Energy ◯

Study **Figure 4**, a map showing daily calorie intake per capita in the world in 2015.

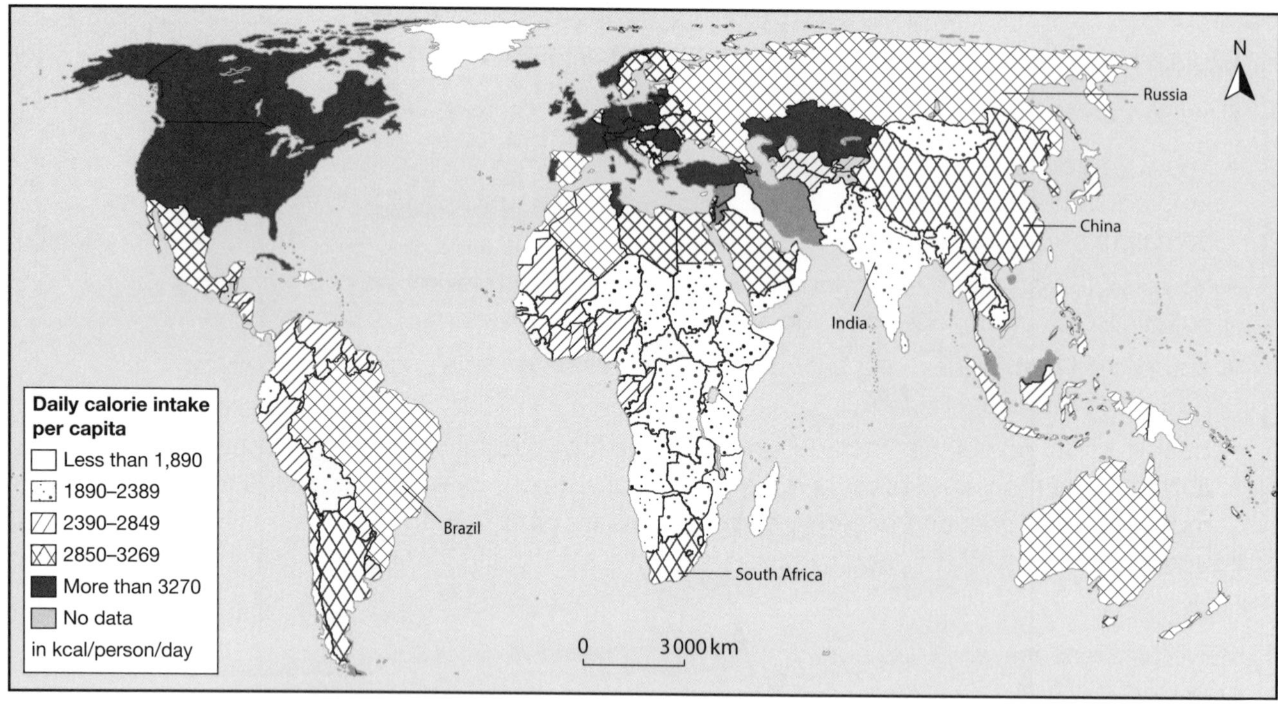

Figure 4

1. What was the range of daily calorie intake per capita in India?

   Shade **one** circle only. (1 mark, ★)

   A Less than 1890 kilocalories ◯

   B 1890–2389 kilocalories ◯

   C 2390–2849 kilocalories ◯

   D 2850–3269 kilocalories ◯

2. Using **Figure 4**, describe the distribution of daily calorie intake per capita in South America. (2 marks, ★)

   ....

   ....

   ....

   ....

(3) Give **two** natural (physical geography) factors that may affect food supply in a country. (2 marks, ★)

Natural factor 1: ....

....

Natural factor 2: ....

....

Make sure that you do not muddle 'small-scale schemes' with 'large-scale schemes'. Also, make sure you know what is meant by the term 'sustainability'.

WORKIT!

Explain how small-scale schemes can create sustainable food supplies. (6 marks, ★★★)

How to tackle this question:

- You will need to recall the example of a sustainable small-scale scheme that you have studied. In the accompanying AQA GCSE Geography Revision Guide, the case study is Jamalpur in Bangladesh.
- You should also be able to bring into your answer other relevant ways of achieving sustainable food supplies through small-scale schemes.
- You should make clear links between the features of the small-scale schemes and how they bring about sustainability.
- Sustainability points may include: ensuring that food supplies exist throughout a year and from year to year; reducing hunger and malnutrition; minimising damage to soils and reducing water use; and ensuring some income for poor farmers.

(4) Give **two** reasons why food consumption is increasing in the world. (2 marks, ★)

Reason 1: ....

....

Reason 2: ....

....

(5) Explain how the impacts of food insecurity cause difficulties for poorer people. (6 marks, ★★★)

....

....

....

....

....

....

....

....

....

....

NAILIT!

- Remember to identify the **command word** or **phrase** in a question. In Question 5, this is *Explain*. 'Explain' means to set out the reasons.
- Identify the **key geographical ideas** in a question. In Question 5, these are *impacts of food insecurity* and *poorer people*.
- Circle both the command words or phrases and the key geographical ideas in questions to help keep you on track.

Water

Study **Figure 5**, a map showing water stress in the densely populated river basins of South and East Asia.

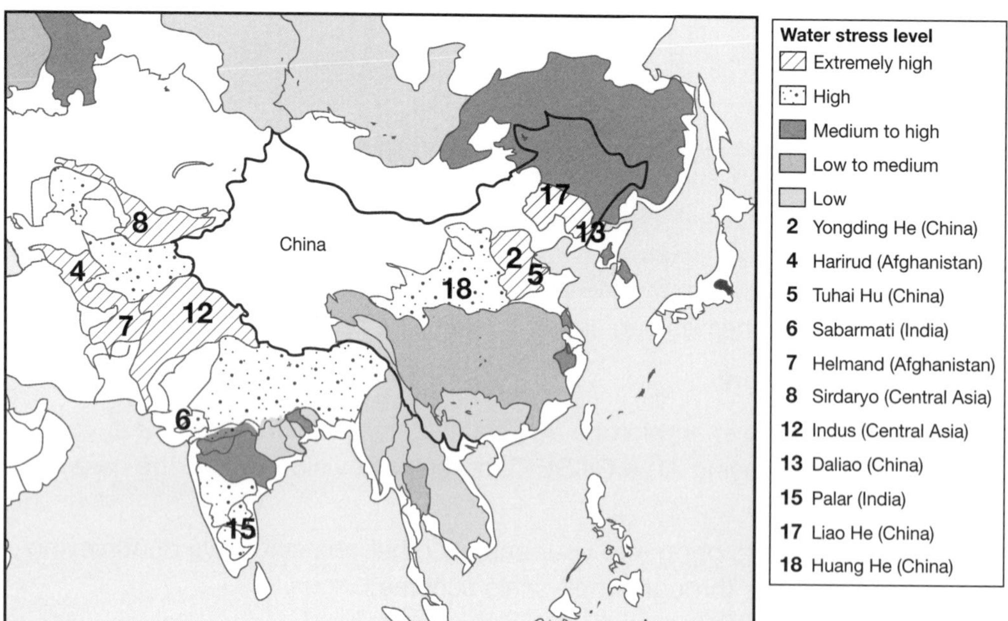

Figure 5

1. What was the water stress level in the Indus River basin?

   Shade **one** circle only. (1 mark, ★)

   A Low to medium stress ◯

   B Medium to high stress ◯

   C High stress ◯

   D Extremely high stress ◯

> Remember, answering multiple-choice questions should be quick. Aim to spend no more than one minute of exam time to work out the answer to this type of question.

2. Using **Figure 5**, describe the distribution of water stress in river basins in China. (2 marks, ★)

   ....

   ....

   ....

   ....

3. Give **two** reasons why water consumption is increasing in the world. (2 marks, ★)

   Reason 1: ....

   ....

   Reason 2: ....

   ....

Make sure that you do not muddle 'small-scale schemes' with 'large-scale schemes'. Also, make sure you know what is meant by the term 'sustainability'.

WORKIT!

Explain how small-scale schemes can create sustainable water supplies. (6 marks, ★★★)

How to tackle this question:

- You will need to recall the example of a sustainable small-scale scheme that you have studied. In the accompanying AQA GCSE Geography Revision Guide, the case study is Hitosa in Ethiopia.
- You should also be able to bring into your answer other relevant ways of achieving sustainable water supplies through small-scale schemes.
- You should make clear links between the features of the small-scale schemes and how they bring about sustainability.
- Sustainability points may include: ensuring reliable water supplies throughout a year and from year to year; maximising water storage and minimising water wastage; ensuring that water is clean so that people are healthier; ensuring that clean water is shared fairly between all people; and keeping costs of water supply low.

4. Give **two** reasons why groundwater management helps to create sustainable water supplies. (2 marks, ★)

Reason 1: ....

....

Reason 2: ....

....

NAILIT!

- Remember to identify the **command word** or **phrase** in a question. In Question 5, this is *Explain*. 'Explain' means to set out the reasons.
- Identify the **key geographical ideas** in a question. In Question 5, these are *impacts of water insecurity* and *poorer people*.
- Circle both the command words or phrases and the key geographical ideas in questions to help keep you on track.

5. Explain how the impacts of water insecurity cause difficulties for poorer people. (6 marks, ★★★)

....

....

....

....

....

....

....

....

Energy

Study **Figure 6**, a map showing energy access and security for countries in 2015.

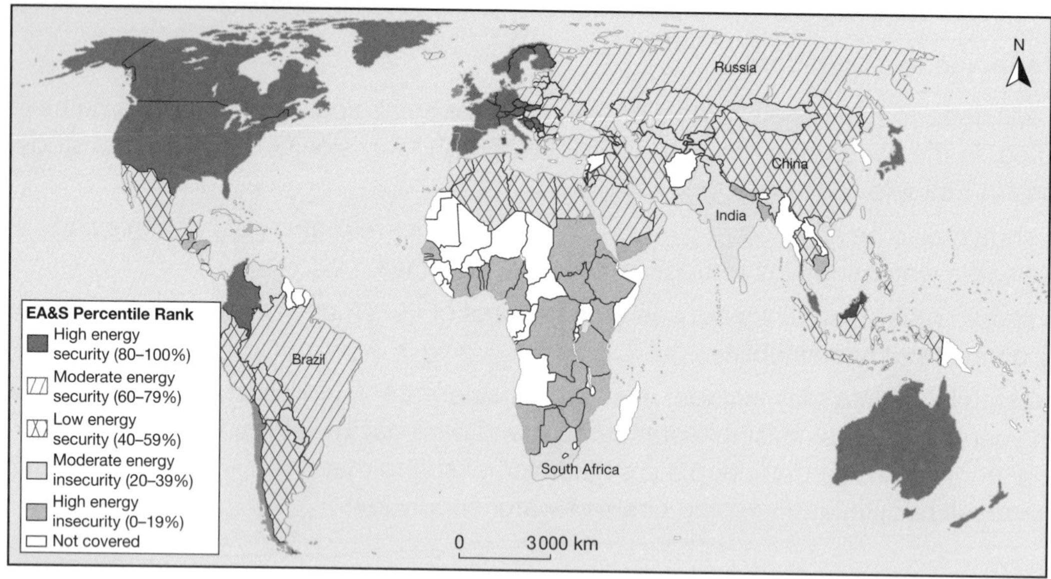

Figure 6

① What was the energy access and security performance level of China in 2015?

Shade **one** circle only. (1 mark, ★)

A 0–19% ◯

B 20–39% ◯

C 40–59% ◯

D 60–79% ◯

② Using **Figure 6**, describe the distribution of energy access and security performance levels in South America in 2015. (2 marks, ★)

....

....

....

....

③ Give **two** reasons why home design can help to create sustainable energy supplies. (2 marks, ★)

Reason 1: ....

....

Reason 2: ....

....

NAILIT!

- Remember to identify the **command word** or **phrase** in a question. In Question 4, this is *Explain*. 'Explain' means to set out the reasons.
- Identify the **key geographical ideas** in a question. In Question 4, these are *impacts of energy insecurity* and *poorer people*.
- Circle both the command words or phrases and the key geographical ideas in questions to help keep you on track.

4 Explain how the impacts of energy insecurity cause difficulties for poorer people. (6 marks, ★★★)

....

....

....

....

....

....

....

....

....

....

....

....

5 Give **two** reasons why energy consumption is increasing in the world. (2 marks, ★)

Reason 1: ....

....

Reason 2: ....

....

Make sure that you do not muddle 'small-scale schemes' with 'large-scale schemes'. Also, make sure you know what is meant by the term 'sustainability'.

WORKIT!

Explain how small-scale renewable energy schemes can create sustainable energy supplies. (6 marks, ★★★)

How to tackle this question:

- You will need to recall the example of a sustainable small-scale scheme that you have studied. In the accompanying AQA GCSE Geography Revision Guide, the case study is Chambamontera in Peru.
- You should also be able to bring into your answer other relevant ways of achieving sustainable energy supplies through small-scale schemes.
- You should make clear links between the features of the small-scale schemes and how they bring about sustainability.
- Sustainability points may include: ensuring a reliable energy supply; low set-up and maintenance costs for local people; low energy costs for local people; use of renewable energy sources that minimise negative impacts on the local and wider environment; and improvements in health levels through lower pollution.

Paper 1 Section A: The challenge of natural hazards

Answer all questions in this section.

Question 1 The challenge of natural hazards

Study **Figure 1**, a graph showing changes in sea surface temperature and hurricane strength.

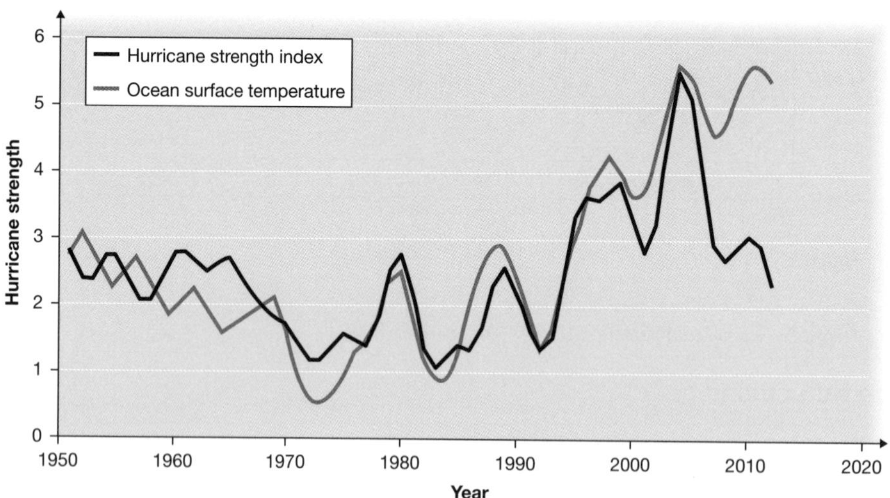

Figure 1

1.1 Describe **one** change in the sea surface temperature shown in Figure 1.

....

....

....

....

[2 marks]

1.2 Outline **one** reason why sea temperatures have changed over time.

....

....

....

....

[2 marks]

Study **Figure 2**, a graph showing changes in global temperature, 1880–2014.

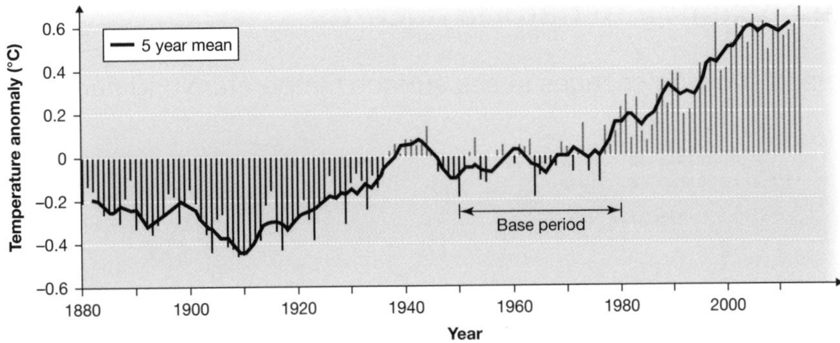

Figure 2

1.3 Using **Figure 2**, which **two** statements are true?

Shade **two** circles only.

A Global temperature has increased since 1880. ◯

B Global temperature was lower in 2000 than it was in 1880. ◯

C At its maximum, the global temperature was approximately 0.6°C above the base temperature. ◯

D At its minimum, the global temperature was approximately 0.6°C below the base temperature. ◯

E The global temperature starts to decrease from 1980. ◯

[2 marks]

1.4 Explain the natural causes of climate change.

....

....

....

....

....

....

....

....

....

....

....

....

[6 marks]

Study **Figure 3**, a map showing the track of Hurricane Katrina in 2005.

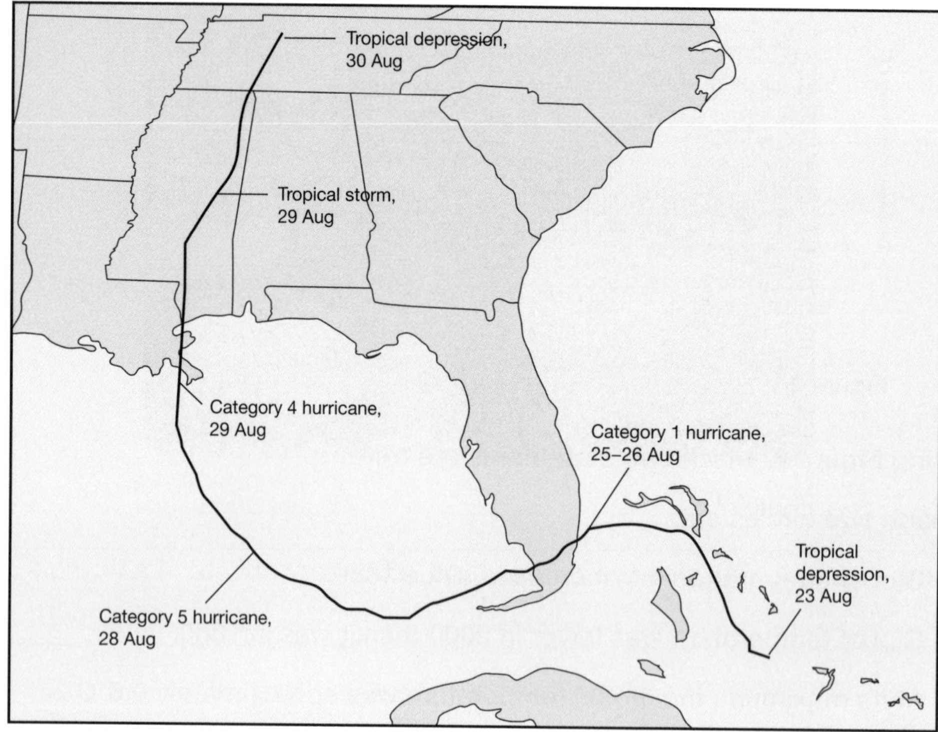

Figure 3

1.5 Describe the direction of the track of Hurricane Katrina in **Figure 3.**

....

....

....

....

[2 marks]

1.6 Describe **one** feature of a tropical storm.

....

....

....

....

[2 marks]

Study **Figure 4**, a photograph showing an area affected by Typhoon Haiyan.

Figure 4

1.7 Using **Figure 4,** describe the primary and secondary effects of a tropical storm.

....

....

....

....

....

....

....

....

[4 marks]

1.8 State **two** ways in which climate change might affect tropical storms.

Effect 1: ....

....

Effect 2: ....

....

[2 marks]

1.9 Choose **either** a volcanic eruption **or** an earthquake.

Evaluate the success of responses to this tectonic hazard in two areas with contrasting levels of wealth.

[9 marks + 3 SPaG marks]

Use a separate sheet of paper to write your answer to this question. State your chosen tectonic hazard at the start of your answer.

Paper 1 Section B: The living world

Answer all questions in this section.

Question 2 The living world

Study **Figure 5**, which shows part of a tropical rainforest food web.

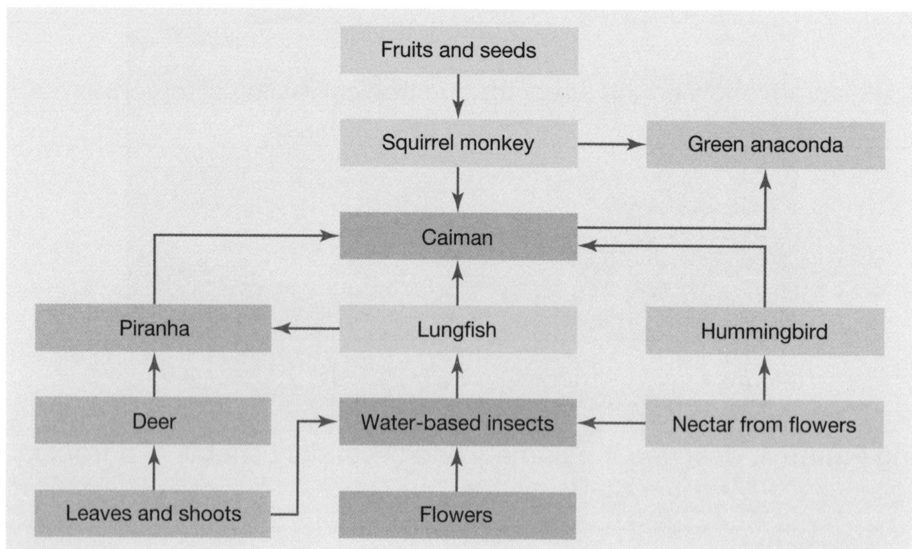

Figure 5

2.1 Using **Figure 5**, which one of the following statements is correct?
Shade **one** circle only.

A The deer eat the piranha. ◯

B The green anaconda eats squirrel monkeys and caimans. ◯

C The caimans eat green anacondas and hummingbirds. ◯

D The water-based insects get their food from the lungfish. ◯

[1 mark]

2.2 Describe what would happen in the food web shown in **Figure 5** if the caiman became extinct.

....

....

....

....

[2 marks]

2.3 Which **one** of the following statements correctly describes the characteristics of a hot desert?
Shade **one** circle only.

A Large average temperature range during a year (−25°C to +10°C) and low precipitation (approximately 500 mm a year). ◯

B Very small average temperature range during a year (27°C to 30°C) and high precipitation (approximately 2500 mm a year). 

C Small average temperature range during a year (20°C to 30°C) and very low precipitation (approximately 125 mm a year).

D Moderate average temperature range during a year (5°C to 18°C) and moderate precipitation (approximately 1500 mm a year). 

[1 mark]

Study **Figure 6**, a diagram showing the structure of a tropical rainforest in northern Australia.

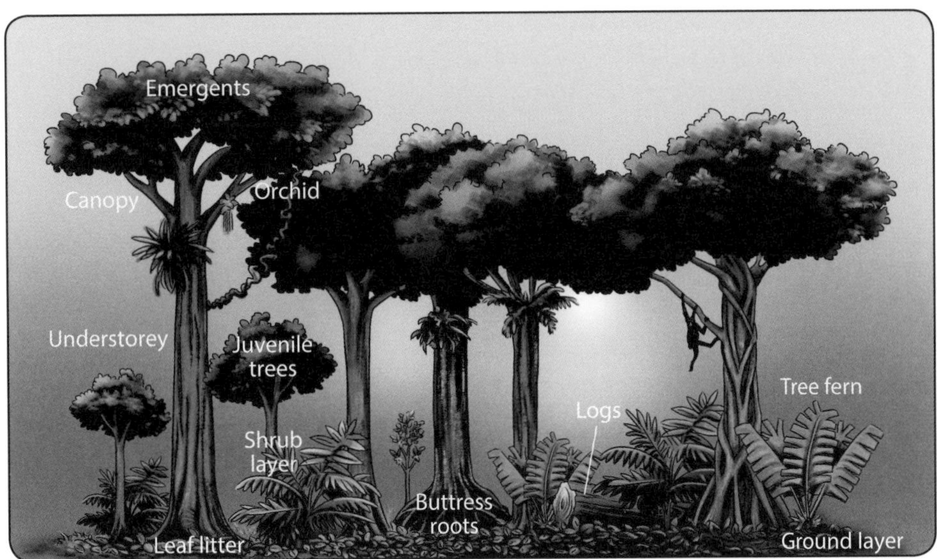

Figure 6

2.4 **Describe and explain the structure of the tropical rainforest shown in Figure 6.**

....

....

....

....

....

....

....

....

....

....

....

....

[6 marks]

Study **Figure 7**, a graph showing deforestation in the Amazon tropical rainforest, Brazil, from 1988 to 2014.

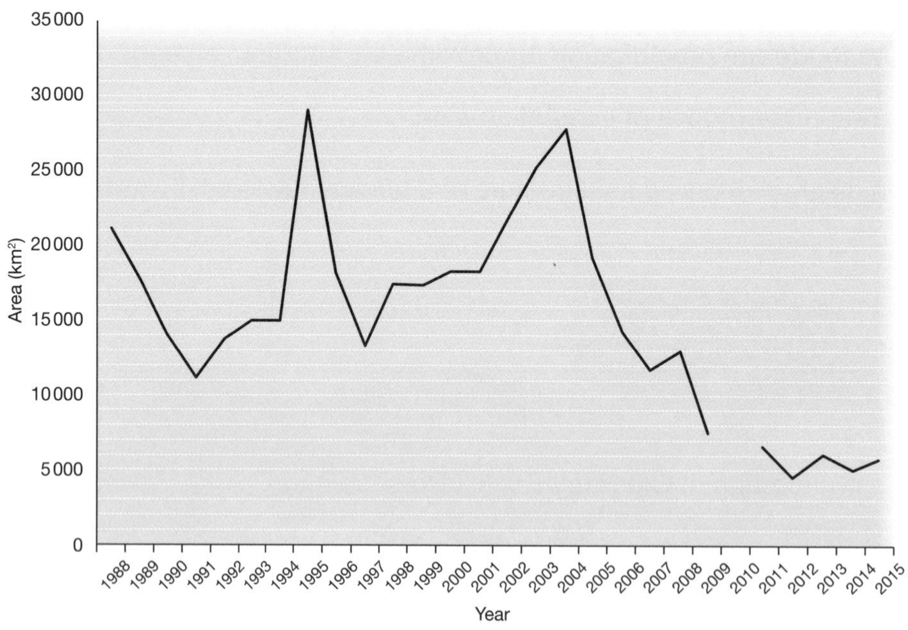

Figure 7

2.5 In 2010, the deforestation rate was 7000 km^2. Plot this on **Figure 7** and complete the line. **[1 mark]**

2.6 In which year was the highest rate of deforestation?

.... **[1 mark]**

2.7 Outline **one** impact of deforestation on the economic development of a country you have studied with a tropical rainforest ecosystem.

....

....

....

.... **[2 marks]**

2.8 Suggest **one** way in which debt reduction can help make tropical rainforests more sustainable.

....

....

....

.... **[2 marks]**

2.9 For a hot desert environment **or** cold environment you have studied, to what extent has technology helped balance economic development and conservation in the environment? **[9 marks]**

Use a separate sheet of paper to write your answer to this question. State your chosen environment at the start of your answer.

Paper 1 Section C: Physical landscapes in the UK

Answer **two** questions from the following:

Question 3 (Coasts), Question 4 (Rivers), Question 5 (Glacial)

Question 3: Coastal landscapes in the UK

3.1 Describe **one** process of coastal erosion.

....

....

....

....

[2 marks]

Study **Figure 8**, a photograph of Old Harry Rocks, Dorset.

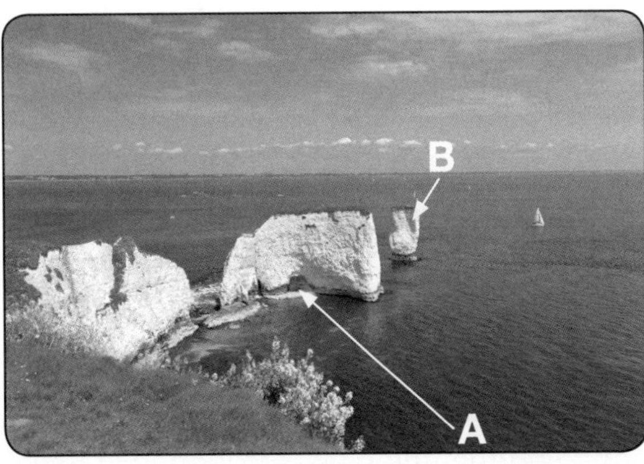

Figure 8

3.2 Using **Figure 8,** identify the coastal features shown at **A** and **B.**

Feature **A:** ....

Feature **B:** ....

[2 marks]

3.3 Using **Figure 8,** explain how coastal feature **B** was formed.

....

....

....

....

....

....

....

....

[4 marks]

Study **Figure 9**, a photograph of coastal defences at Scarborough.

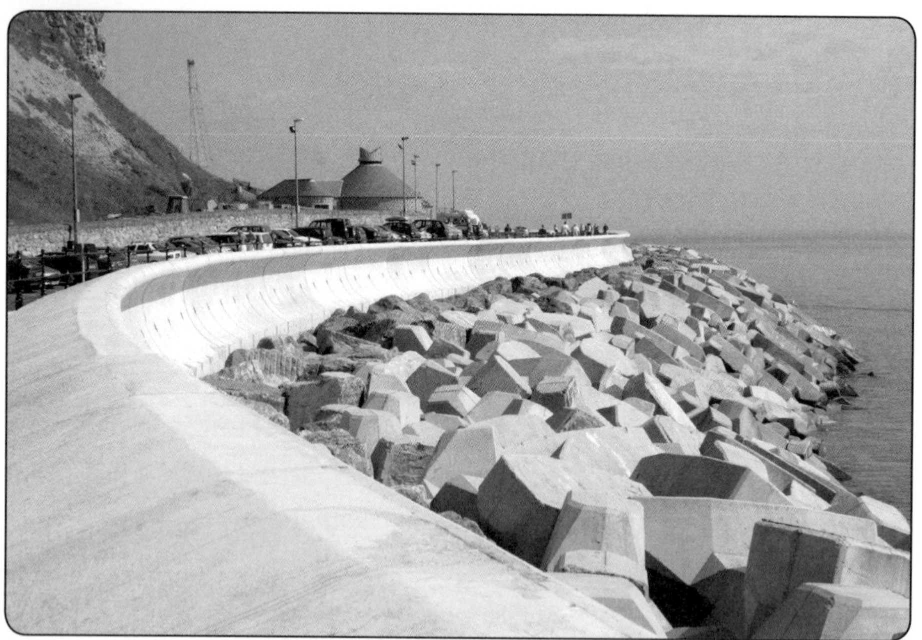

Figure 9

3.4 Name **one** coastal defence shown in **Figure 9**.

....

[1 mark]

3.5 Using **Figure 9** and your own knowledge, explain the advantages and disadvantages of hard engineering to protect the coastline.

....

....

....

....

....

....

....

....

....

....

....

....

[6 marks]

Question 4: River landscapes in the UK

Study **Figure 10**, showing a section of a river.

4.1 What stage of the river's long profile is shown in **Figure 10**?

....

....

....

....

[1 mark]

Figure 10

Study **Figure 11**, a photograph of a meandering river.

Figure 11

4.2 Explain the formation of the landform shown in **Figure 11.**

....

....

....

....

....

....

....

....

[4 marks]

4.3 Describe **two** causes of river flooding.

Cause 1: ....

....

Cause 2: ....

....

[4 marks]

4.4 Using a named example, explain the costs and benefits of a flood management scheme in the UK.

....

....

....

....

....

....

....

....

....

....

....

....

[6 marks]

Question 5: Glacial landscapes in the UK

Study **Figure 12**, a photograph showing a glacial landform.

5.1 Name the glacial landform shown at **A** in **Figure 12.**

....

....

....

....

[1 mark]

A

Figure 12

Study **Figure 13**, a 1: 50 000 Ordnance Survey map extract of part of the Lake District.

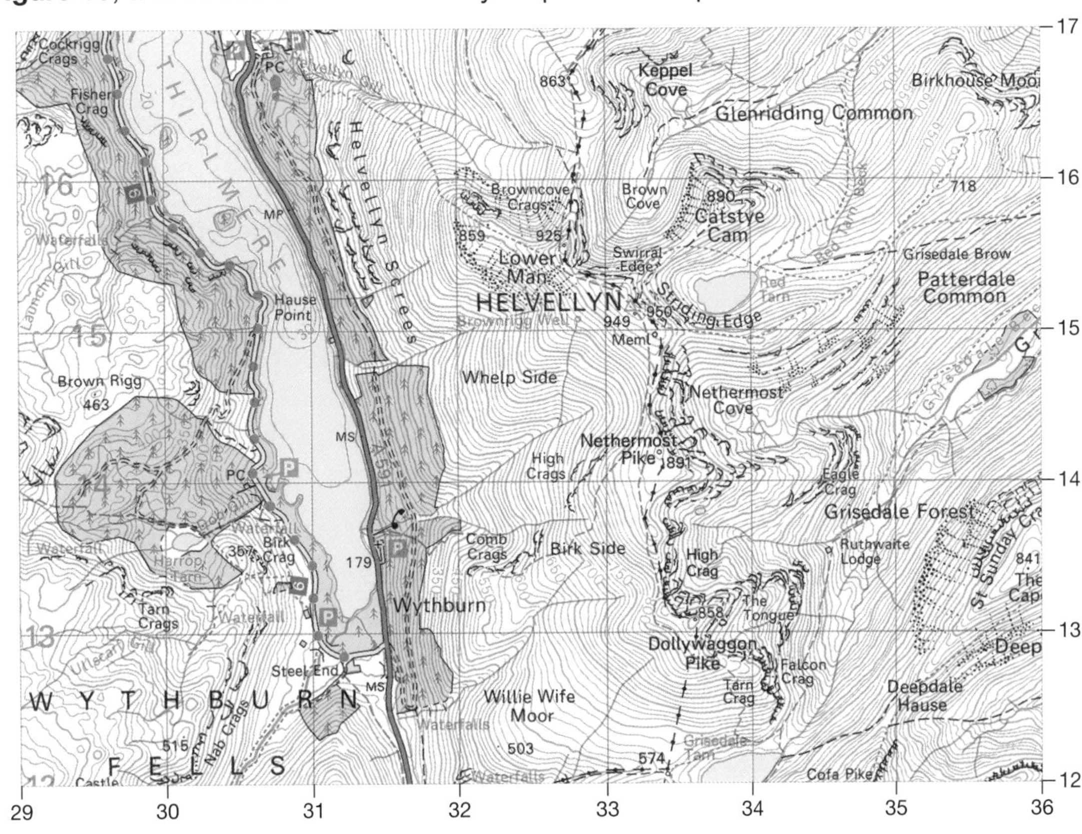

Figure 13

5.2 Identify the glacial feature at grid reference 345151. Shade **one** circle only:

A truncated spur

B glacial trough

C arête

D moraine 

[1 mark]

Study **Figure 14**, a photograph of the glacial lake in grid square 3415 in **Figure 13**.

Figure 14

5.3 Using **Figures 13** and **14**, name the lake shown in the photograph.

....

[1 mark]

5.4 Describe **two** ways in which glaciated areas can create economic opportunities.

....

....

[2 marks]

5.5 Suggest why you may get conflicts when developing a glacial upland area.

....

....

....

....

....

....

....

....

[4 marks]

5.6 Explain how different erosional landforms may be created in a glacial environment.

....

....

....

....

....

....

....

....

....

....

....

....

[6 marks]

Paper 2 Section A: Urban issues and challenges

Answer all questions in this section.

Question 1: Urban issues and challenges

Study **Figure 1**, a map from 2005 showing the world's largest megacities.

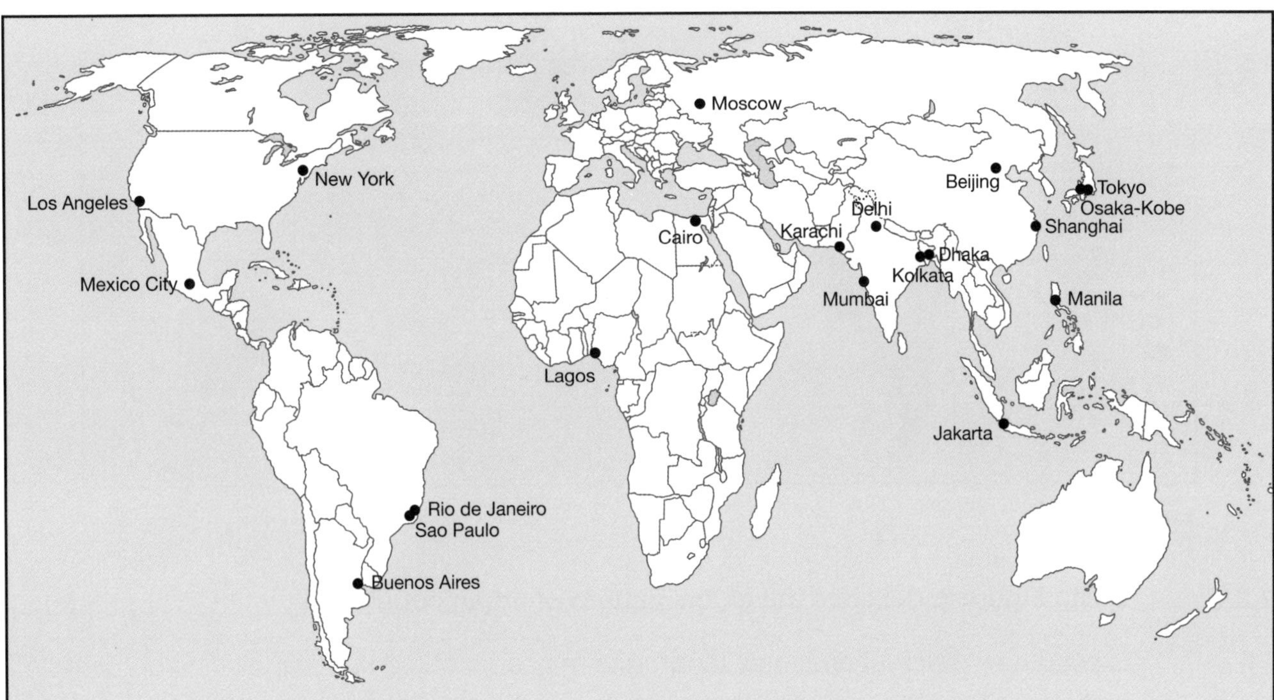

Figure 1

1.1 Using **Figure 1**, which **two** of the following statements are true?

Shade **two** circles only.

A Most of the world's largest megacities are located in HICs. ◯

B Most of the world's largest megacities are located in Asia. ◯

C Most of the world's megacities are located in LICs or NEEs. ◯

D Europe has the megacities with the largest population in the world. ◯

E Africa does not have any megacities. ◯

[2 marks]

Study **Figure 2**, a map showing the percentage of urban population in different parts of the world.

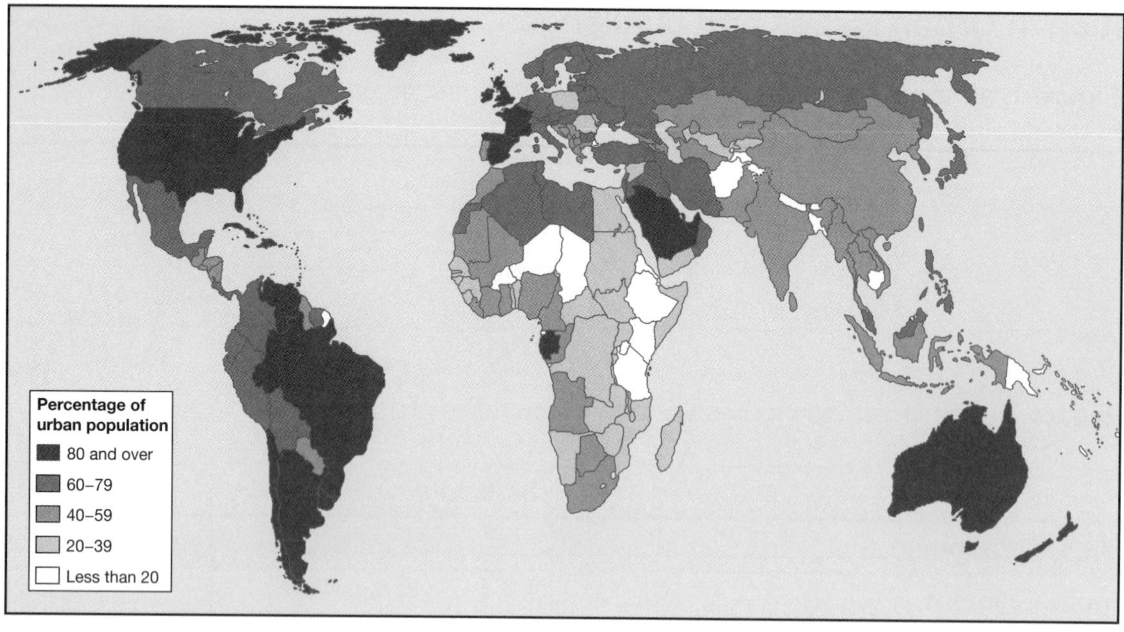

Figure 2

1.2 Using **Figure 2**, describe the global pattern of urban population.

....

....

....

....

[2 marks]

1.3 Suggest **two** reasons why the rate of urban growth is increasing more rapidly in developing countries.

Reason 1: ....

....

Reason 2: ....

....

[2 marks]

1.4 Discuss the social and economic effects of rapid population growth on a city in a lower income country (LIC) or newly emerging economy (NEE) you have studied.

....

....

....

....

....

....

....

....

....

....

....

....

[6 marks]

Study **Figure 3**, a table comparing two London boroughs in 2015.

	Richmond upon Thames	Newham
Life expectancy	83 years	77 years
Unemployment	3.8%	8.5%
Pupils achieving 5 A*–C grades at GCSE	70%	57%
Average household income	£46 000	£28 000

Figure 3

1.5 **Using Figure 3, describe two differences in levels of deprivation between Richmond upon Thames and Newham.**

Difference 1: ....

....

....

....

Difference 2: ....

....

....

....

[4 marks]

1.6 State **two** ways in which traffic can be managed in an urban area.

1: ....

....

2: ....

....

[2 marks]

1.7 Using a named example, explain how a city can reduce its use of resources to improve its sustainability.

....

....

....

....

....

....

....

....

....

....

....

....

[6 marks]

1.8 Evaluate the success of a UK regeneration project you have studied.

[9 marks + 3 SPaG marks]

Use a separate sheet of paper to write your answer to this question.

Answer all questions in this section.

Question 2: The changing economic world

Study **Figure 4**, a world map showing life expectancy in countries of the world in 2015.

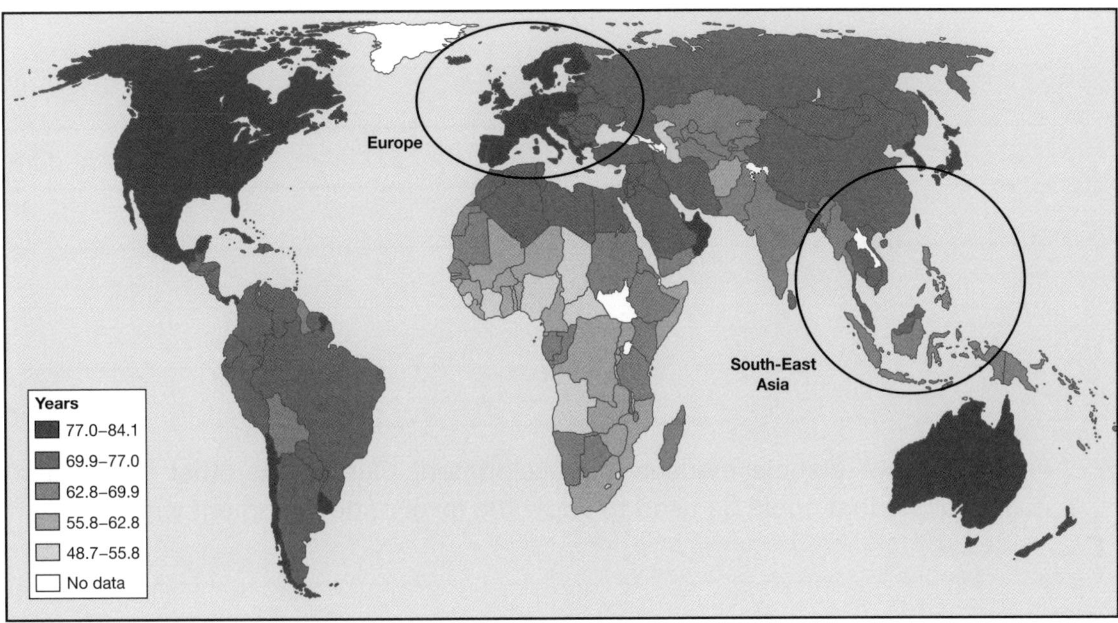

Figure 4

2.1 **Using Figure 4, compare the life expectancies in Europe with those in South-East Asia.**

....

....

....

....

[2 marks]

Study **Figure 5**, a scatter graph showing GNI per capita (person) and infant mortality rates for selected countries in 2015.

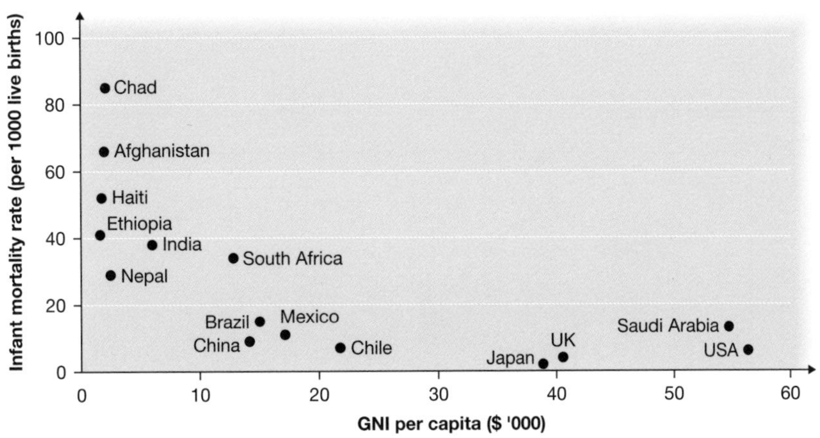

Figure 5

2.2 Using **Figure 5**, explain how infant mortality rates can be used to show differences in quality of life between countries.

....

....

....

....

....

....

....

....

[4 marks]

2.3 **Figure 5** shows a social measure of development. Outline **one** other measure of quality of life that could be used to show the level of development within a country.

....

....

....

....

[2 marks]

Study **Figure 6**, maps showing the migration of people from the UK and Nigeria to other continents and countries.

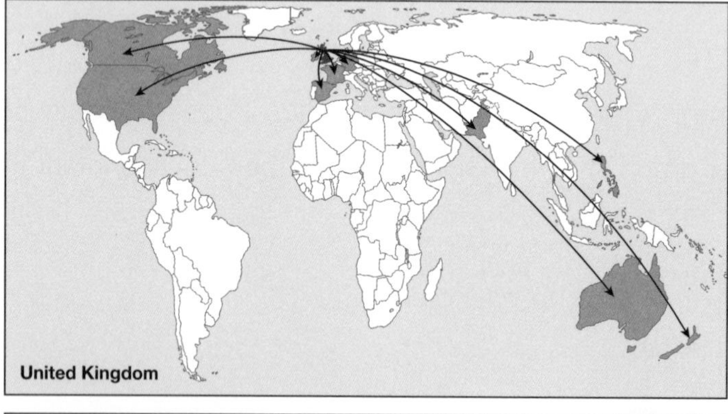

Figure 6

2.4 Using **Figure 6**, name **one** continent that is receiving people from the UK.

....

[1 mark]

2.5 Using **Figure 6**, explain why the patterns of migration out of the UK and out of Nigeria are different.

....

....

....

....

....

....

....

....

[4 marks]

2.6 Give **two** reasons why there is a disparity in the wealth of people within countries.

Reason 1: ....

....

Reason 2: ....

....

[2 marks]

Study **Figure 7**, a line graph showing changes in the UK's industrial employment.

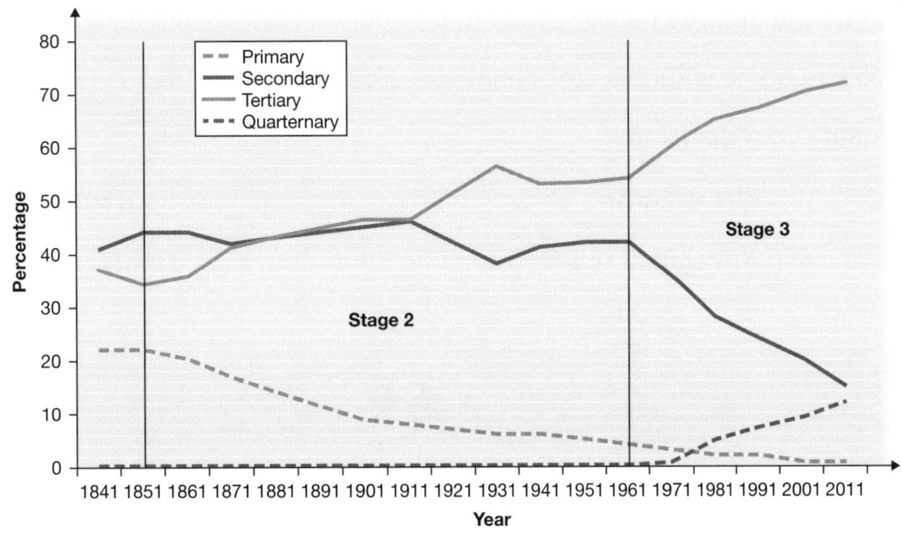

Figure 7

2.7 Compare the changes to primary and tertiary employment during Stage 2 in **Figure 7**.

....

....

[1 mark]

2.8 Using **Figure 7**, calculate the percentage difference between primary and quaternary employment in 2011.

....

....

[1 mark]

2.9 Outline **one** way in which globalisation has helped to increase tertiary employment and business in the UK.

....

....

....

....

[2 marks]

2.10 Suggest **one** problem that deindustrialisation has caused in the UK.

....

....

....

....

[2 marks]

2.11 'Industrial activity can be made to be environmentally sustainable in the UK.'

Do you agree with this statement? Yes ☐ No ☐

Justify your decision.

[9 marks + 3 SPaG marks]

Use a separate sheet of paper to write your answer to this question.

Paper 2 Section C: The challenge of resource management

Answer Question 3 and either Question 4 or Question 5 or Question 6.

Question 3: The challenge of resource management

Study **Figure 8**, which provides information about undernourishment and malnutrition in the world.

3.1 What has been the decline in undernourishment since 1992?

[1 mark]

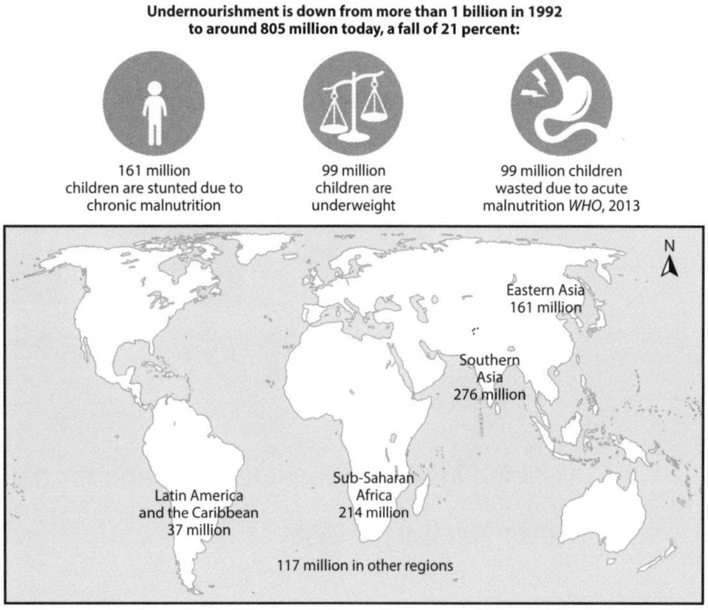

Undernourishment is down from more than 1 billion in 1992 to around 805 million today, a fall of 21 percent:

161 million children are stunted due to chronic malnutrition

99 million children are underweight

99 million children wasted due to acute malnutrition *WHO*, 2013

N

Eastern Asia 161 million

Southern Asia 276 million

Sub-Saharan Africa 214 million

Latin America and the Caribbean 37 million

117 million in other regions

Figure 8

3.2 Using **Figure 8,** describe the distribution of undernourishment by world region.

[2 marks]

3.3 Explain why investing in better nutrition is a way of increasing the chances of a country's development.

[6 marks]

Study **Figure 9**, a graph showing the UK's recent production of primary fuels from its own resources.

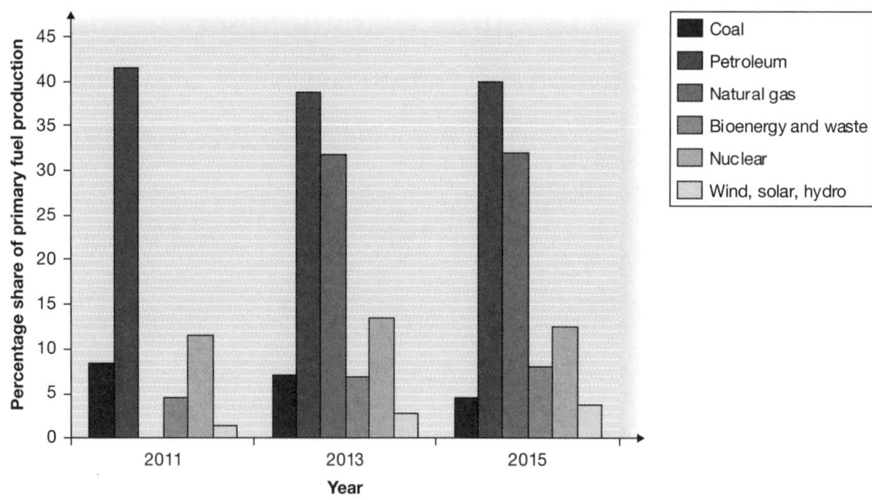

Figure 9

3.4 Using **Figure 9**, complete the graph for natural gas in 2011 using the following data:

2011 Natural gas 33%

[1 mark]

3.5 State the increase in percentage share of primary fuel production of bioenergy and waste between 2011 and 2015.

Shade **one** circle only.

A 3.5% ◯ **C** 6.7% ◯

B 4.4% ◯ **D** 7.9% ◯

[1 mark]

Study **Figure 10**, a graph showing the change in UK electricity generation from renewable sources.

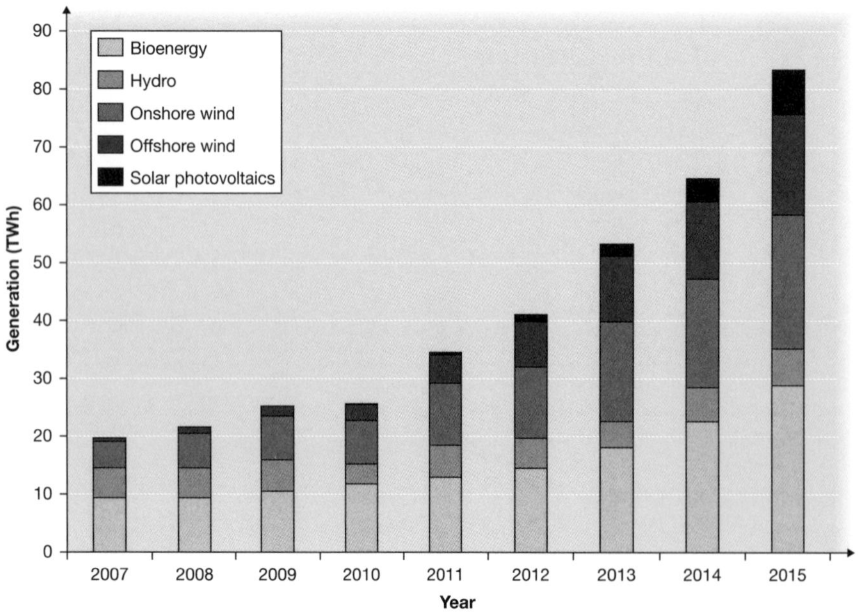

Figure 10

3.6 Using **Figure 10**, suggest why the use of renewable energy sources in the UK is increasing.

....

....

....

....

....

....

[3 marks]

Answer either Question 4 (Food) or Question 5 (Water) or Question 6 (Energy).

Shade the circle below to indicate which optional question you will answer.

Question 4 ◯ Question 5 ◯ Question 6 ◯

Question 4: Food

Study **Figure 11**, a flow line map showing the value of exports of agricultural products from the European Union (EU) in 2014.

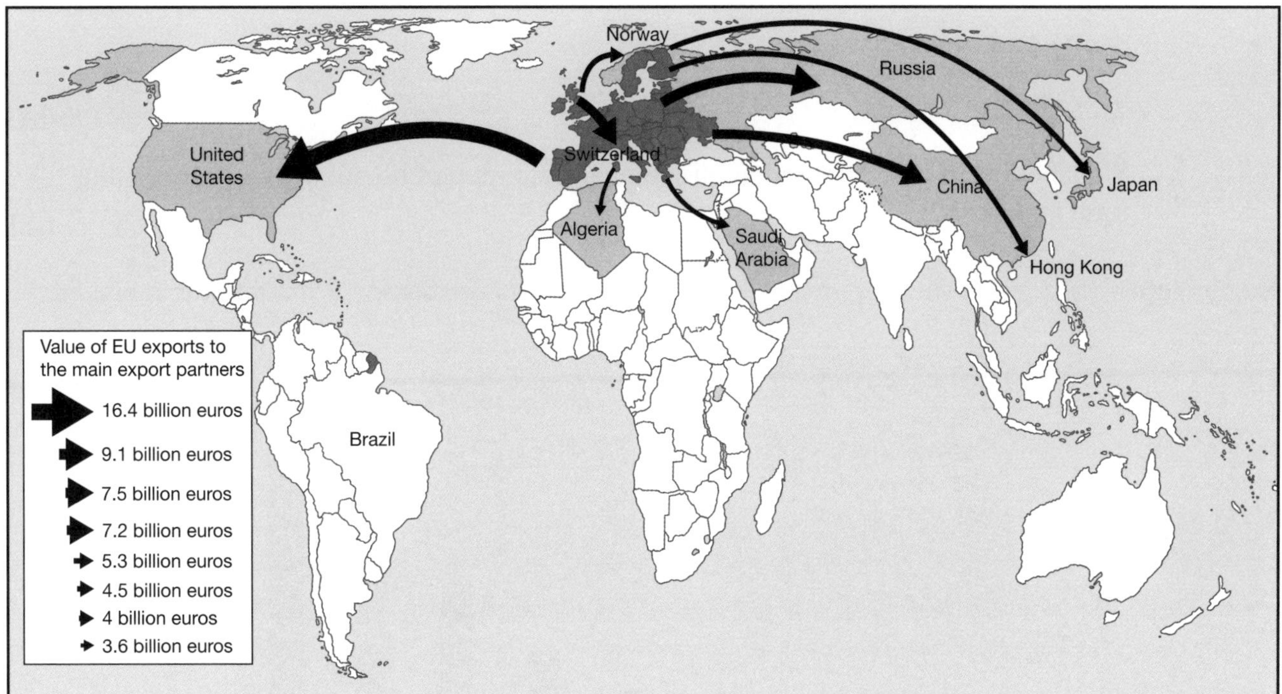

Figure 11

4.1 Using **Figure 11**, what was the approximate value of agricultural exports from the EU to China in 2014?

Shade **one** circle only.

A 16.4 billion euros	◯	**C** 7.2 billion euros	◯
B 9.1 billion euros	◯	**D** 5.3 billion euros	◯

[1 mark]

4.2 Using **Figure 11**, describe the pattern of world agricultural exports from the EU in 2014.

....

....

....

....

[2 marks]

4.3 Give **two** reasons why permaculture is a sustainable way of producing food.

Reason 1: ....

....

Reason 2: ....

....

[2 marks]

4.4 Explain how large-scale agricultural developments can be successful in reducing food insecurity.

....

....

....

....

....

....

....

....

....

....

....

....

[6 marks]

Question 5: Water

Study **Figure 12**, a map showing the amount of water stress in the world.

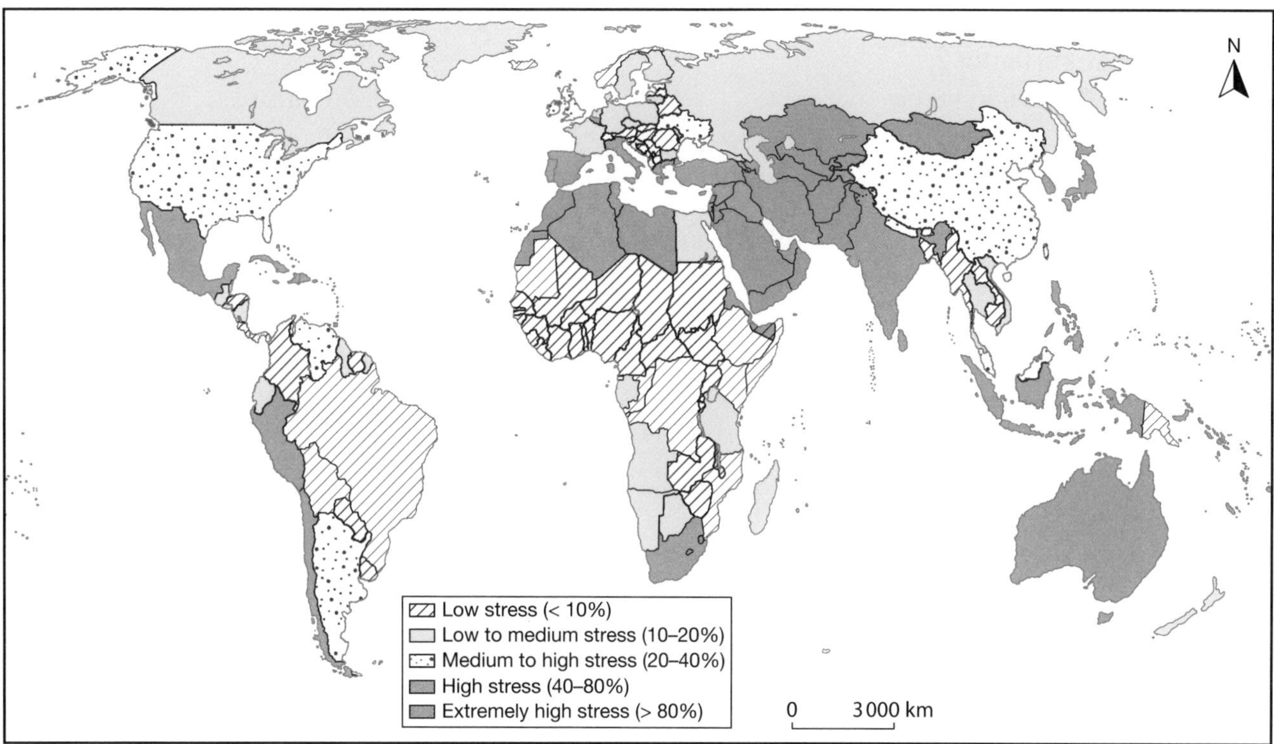

Figure 12

5.1 What was the water stress level in the USA?

Shade **one** circle only.

A Low to medium stress ◯

B Medium to high stress ◯

C High stress ◯

D Extremely high stress ◯

[1 mark]

5.2 Using **Figure 12,** describe the distribution of water stress in South America.

....

....

....

....

[2 marks]

5.3 Give **two** natural factors that may affect the water supply in a country.

Natural factor 1: ....

....

Natural factor 2: ....

....

[2 marks]

5.4 Explain how large-scale water transfer schemes can help to reduce water insecurity.

....

....

....

....

....

....

....

....

....

....

....

....

[6 marks]

Question 6: Energy

Study **Figure 13**, a map showing the percentage share of wind and solar energy of total energy production in 2015.

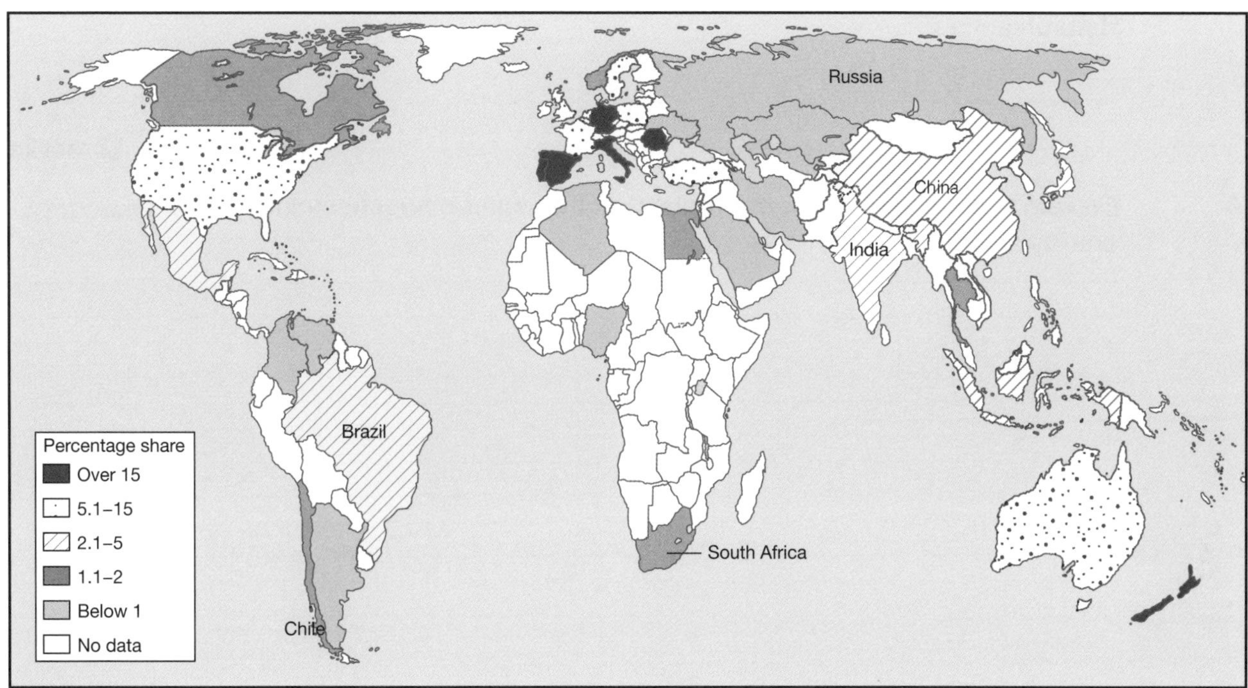

Figure 13

6.1 **What was the share of wind and solar energy production in India?**

Shade one circle only.

A 1.1 to 2% ◯

B 2.1 to 5% ◯

C 5.1 to 15% ◯

D over 15% ◯

[1 mark]

6.2 **Using Figure 13, describe the distribution of wind and solar energy production share in South America.**

....

....

....

....

[2 marks]

6.3 Give **two** reasons why wind energy is a sustainable way of producing energy.

Reason 1: ....

....

Reason 2: ....

....

[2 marks]

6.4 Explain how large-scale fossil fuel extraction can be successful in reducing energy insecurity.

....

....

....

....

....

....

....

....

....

....

....

....

[6 marks]

Resources for Paper 3 Geographical applications: Issue evaluation

To be issued to students 12 weeks before the date of the exam.

This booklet contains four resources as follows:

- **Figure 2** – Trends and patterns in air traffic
- **Figure 3** – Reasons for trends and patterns in UK air traffic
- **Figure 5** – Challenges arising from the trends and patterns in UK air traffic
- **Figure 6** – Possible solutions to the South-East airport capacity problem

Figure 2

Trends and patterns in air traffic

According to World Bank data:

- In 1970, the number of world air transport passengers was fewer than 0.5 billion and the UK's share fewer than 20 million.
- As the number of airports and aircraft has increased, so have passenger numbers. By 2015, the number for the world was nearly 3.5 billion and for the UK was more than 130 million.
- A number of NEE countries have built impressive large airports such as Shanghai and Hong Kong in China, Singapore, and Dubai in the United Arab Emirates (UAE).
- Patterns have been affected by the 2008 economic recession and because the latest generation of aircraft are larger and more fuel-efficient.

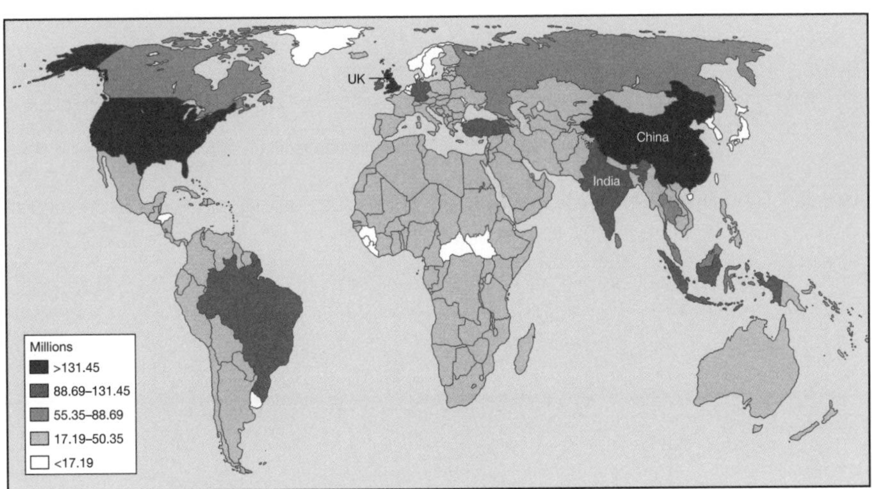

Figure 2.1 Air transport passengers carried by country, 2015

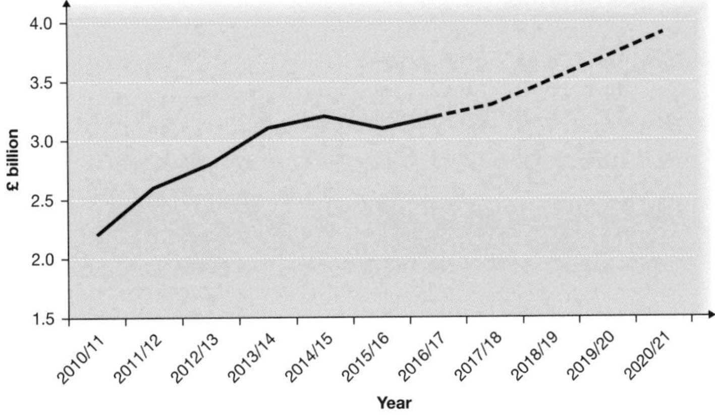

Figure 2.2 UK revenues from Air Passenger Duty (tax) 2010–16 and predictions for the future

Figure 2 continued

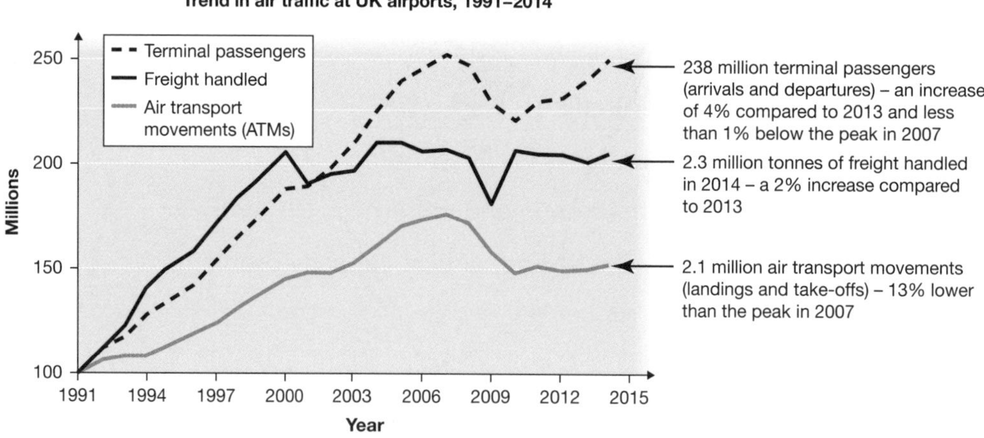

Figure 2.3 Recent UK transport statistics for aviation

Figure 3

Reasons for trends and patterns in UK air traffic

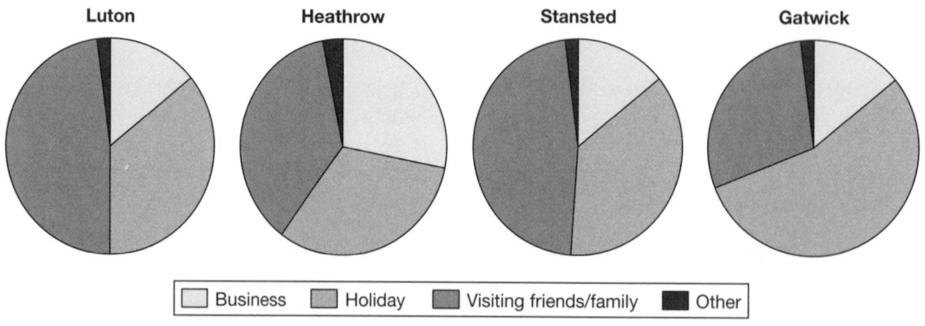

Figure 3.1 The purpose of air travel for passengers using main London airports in 2015

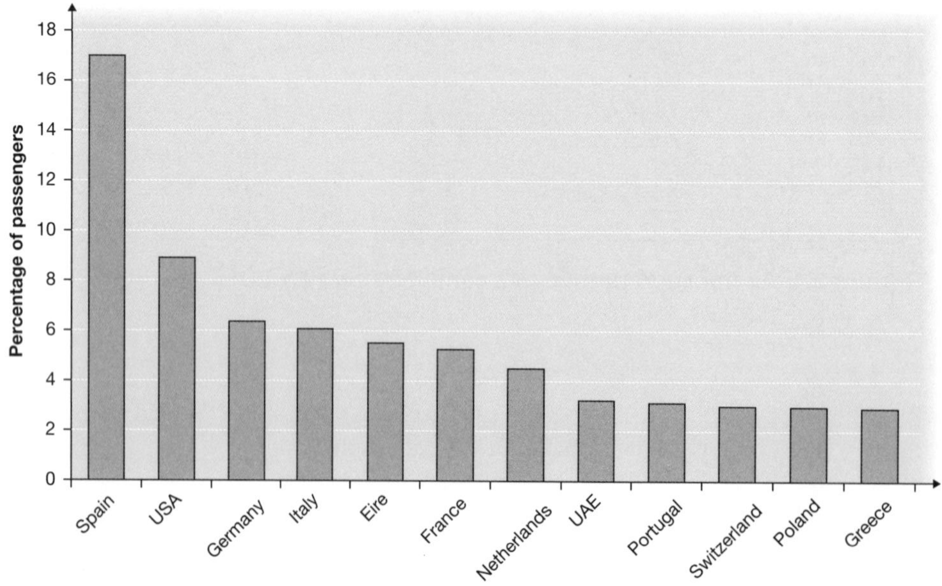

Figure 3.2 UK top 12 arrival and destination countries for air passengers in 2015

Figure 3 continued

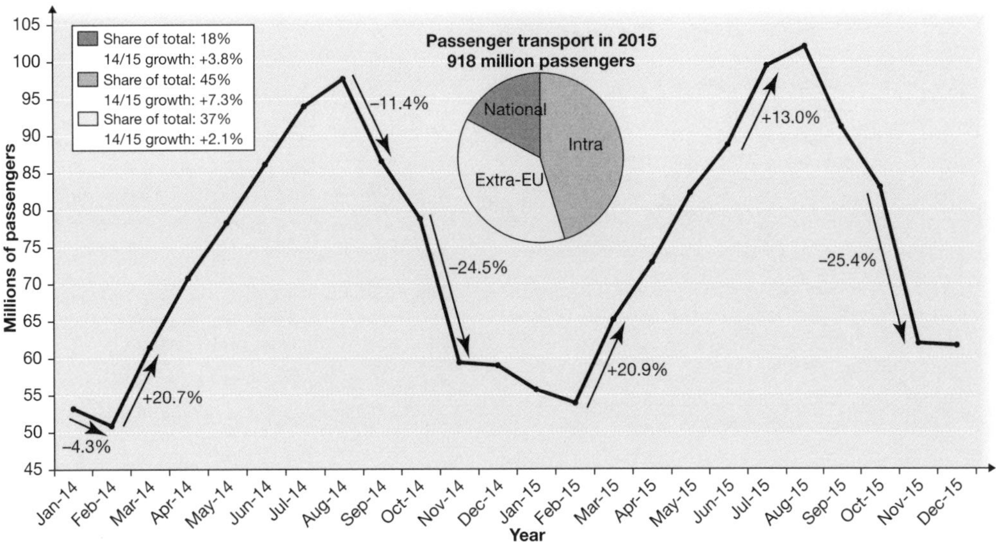

Figure 3.3 European Union monthly change and share of air passengers carried in 2014 and 2015

Figure 5

Challenges arising from the trends and patterns in UK air traffic

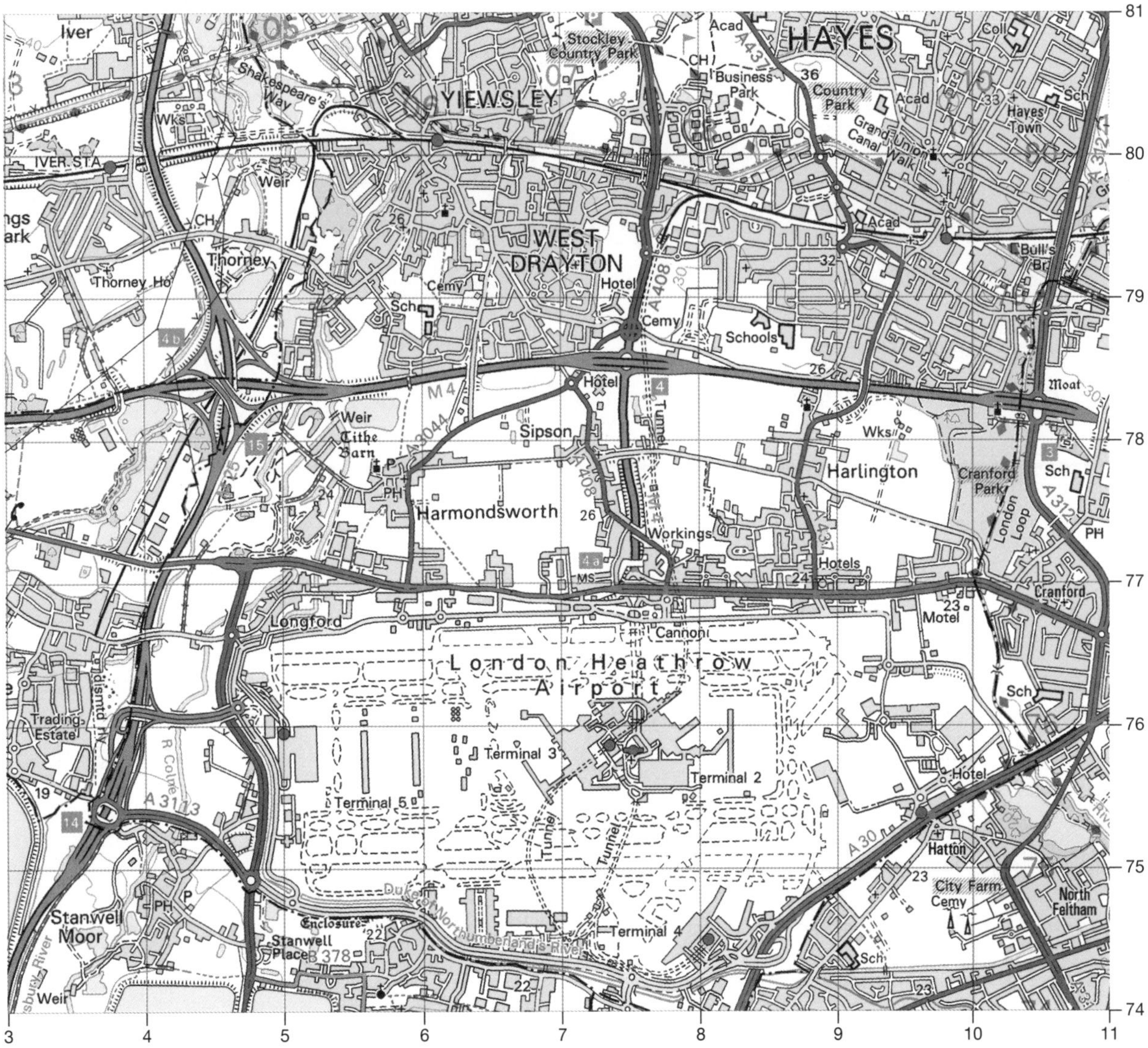

Figure 5.1 A 1: 50 000 Ordnance Survey map extract of the Heathrow airport area

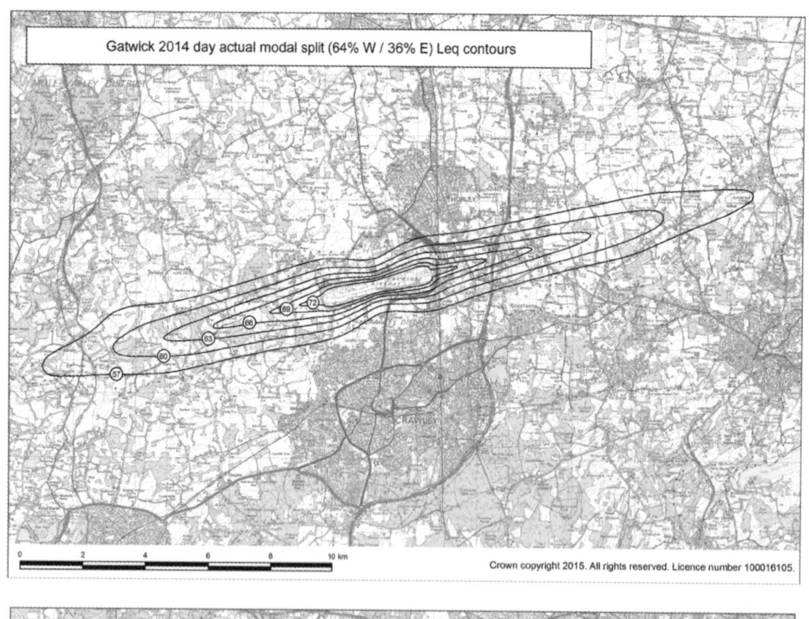

Gatwick airport

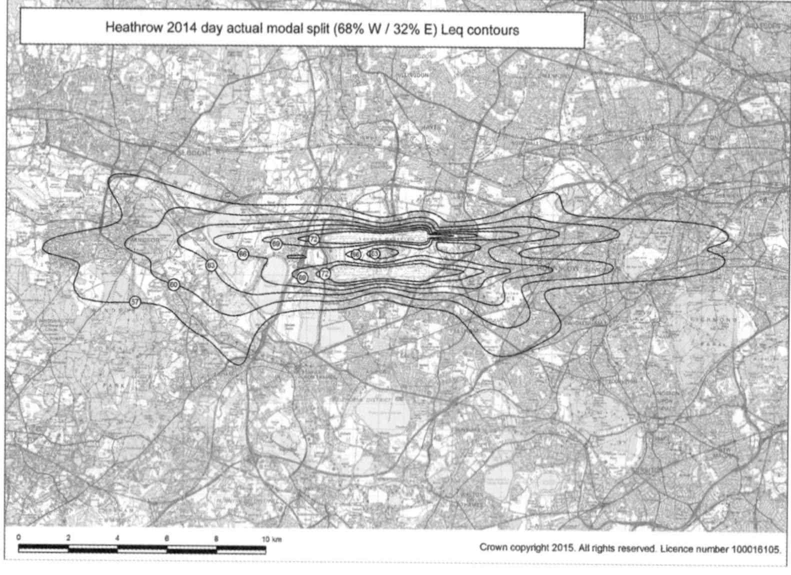

Heathrow airport

Figure 5.2 Noise patterns (in isobels) for Gatwick and Heathrow airports in 2014

The UK aviation situation

Increasing demand

In 2015, Heathrow was the EU's busiest airport, Gatwick was 8th, Stansted 20th and Luton 30th, with the UK's smaller airports increasing their passenger traffic at a faster rate than both Heathrow and Gatwick. As demand grows, the airports will fill until they reach the limits of either terminal or runway capacities. Over 90 per cent of national passenger capacity is expected to be reached by the early 2040s. Forecasts suggest that all the airports in the South-East will be at capacity by 2030 and the larger airports outside the South-East from 2040. The first airports to fill by 2020 will be in the London area, especially Heathrow and Gatwick.

The UK government commissioned a report to recommend where to expand airport capacity in the South-East of the UK. Three options are available:

1. Expand Heathrow airport to the west of London.
2. Expand Gatwick airport to the south of London.
3. Build a new Thames Hub airport to the east of London.

Figure 6

Possible solutions to the South-East airport capacity problem

Expand Heathrow: benefits for the UK

1 It will create over 120 000 new jobs, 42% of these outside the London area.
2 As a hub airport, Heathrow is connected to the rest of the UK and has experience with handling lots of goods.
3 It can double its cargo handling capacity, helping 100 000 more UK companies trade abroad.
4 It can help meet the government target of doubling exports.
5 New airlines will increase competition and so reduce passenger fares.
6 It will be easier for people to travel abroad or within the UK by air.

Figure 6.1 Arguments for Heathrow airport expansion

Only Gatwick can guarantee:

1 **Growth across the UK**: we will create the same economic boost as Heathrow, but a bigger boost to regional connectivity across the UK.
2 **A cap on passenger charges** – we will cap air passenger charges at an inflation-linked £15.
3 **No public subsidy**: we will fund the scheme privately and in full.
4 **Legal air quality**: we will not breach legally binding air quality limits with the new runway.
5 **A cap on those most affected by noise**: we will limit the area of the noise contour most affected by noise to 70 km^2.
6 **Industry-leading compensation**: we will pay £1000 per annum towards the Council Tax of those most affected by noise.

Figure 6.2 Arguments for expanding Gatwick airport

Thames Hub Airport proposal

Reaction to the Airport Commission final report by Foster and Partners

01 July 2015

The only long-term answer to the question posed to the Airports Commission, 'how do we maintain our global aviation hub status?' is a brand new 4-runway 24-hour airport to the east of the capital, the Thames Hub. It is a bold, flexible, future-proof solution which neither Heathrow nor Gatwick will ever achieve.

The expansion of London towards the east has now been reinforced with the approval of Ebbsfleet Garden City and moves toward a Lower Thames crossing – further validating the relocation of the airport to the Isle of Grain. The argument against the relocation of the bird habitat has been diminished with the success of the Wallasea wetlands project further down the estuary.

The Thames Hub airport will deliver the global connectivity that Londoners demand whilst bringing respite to all tormented by aircraft noise. Connecting the UK to new global destinations throughout the day and night, it can be built for a cost of £26 billion including upgraded road and rail services in just 7 years – the same time it will take for a new runway at Heathrow to be squeezed into a London borough. An integrated rail hub will connect services to Europe, London in just 30 minutes and the rest of the UK.

The case for the Thames Hub Airport

- The Thames Hub Airport will be linked to the rest of the UK and Europe by high-speed rail with a 30-minute ride to central London.
- It will be closer to shipping ports for the efficient distribution of goods.
- An integrated rail hub at the terminal will serve 300 000 people a day and cater for the 150-million passengers-per-annum capacity, new 24-hour airport, which will connect the UK to all the emerging economic capitals of the world.
- Air and noise pollution is a quality of life issue and with the capital's population due to expand by 20 per cent over the next two decades, this has become even more pressing. We need to move our hub airport out of our suburbs and unlock the space – equivalent to a new borough – for more homes and jobs within the city.
- The capital is moving east, and the Thames Hub Airport is the obvious answer to the question 'how do we maintain our global aviation hub status?'
- Independent research has shown that in the next decade we need to connect to 55 new destinations across the world to maintain our access to a consistent share of global trade.

Paper 3 Section A: Issue evaluation

Answer all questions in this section.

Study **Figure 1**, a graph showing UK aircraft landings and take-offs between 1970 and 2015. (Note that this graph uses an index based on 1950 = 100).

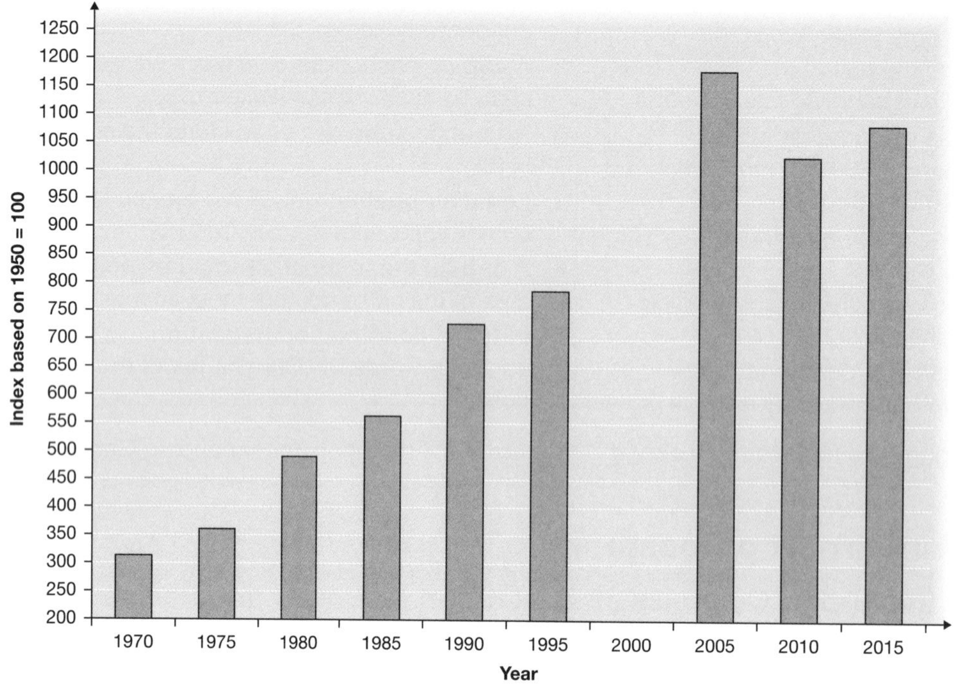

Figure 1

1.1 **Using Figure 1, complete the graph using the following data for UK aircraft landings and take-offs in the year 2000.**

Index for UK aircraft landings and take-offs in 2000 = **1006** **[1 mark]**

Study **Figure 2**, 'Trends and patterns in air traffic', in the resources (pages 97–8).

1.2 **With the help of Figure 2.1, 'Air transport passengers carried by country, 2015', which one of the following statements is correct?**

Shade one circle only.

A The UK was the only country with over 131.45 million passengers. ○

B India and China were in the same passenger number category. ○

C All the countries in South America had between 50.35 and 88.69 million passengers. ○

D The continent of Africa had no country with over 50.35 million passengers. ○

[1 mark]

1.3 **With the help of Figure 2, suggest the benefits that the UK may gain from high volumes of air traffic.**

....

....

....

....

....

....

....

....

....

....

[6 marks]

Study **Figure 3.3**, 'European Union monthly change and share of air passengers carried in 2014 and 2015', in the resources (page 99).

2.1 **In which month of 2014 and 2015 was the number of air passengers in the European Union (EU) at the lowest level?**

....

[1 mark]

Study **Figure 3**, 'Reasons for trends and patterns in UK air traffic', in the resources (pages 98–9).

2.2 **'Holiday air travel has a major influence on the annual pattern of air traffic in the UK.'**

Use Figure 3 and your own understanding to discuss this statement.

....

....

....

....

....

....

....

....

....

....

[6 marks]

Study **Figure 4**, a line graph showing carbon dioxide (CO_2) emissions by UK aviation between 1970 and 2020.

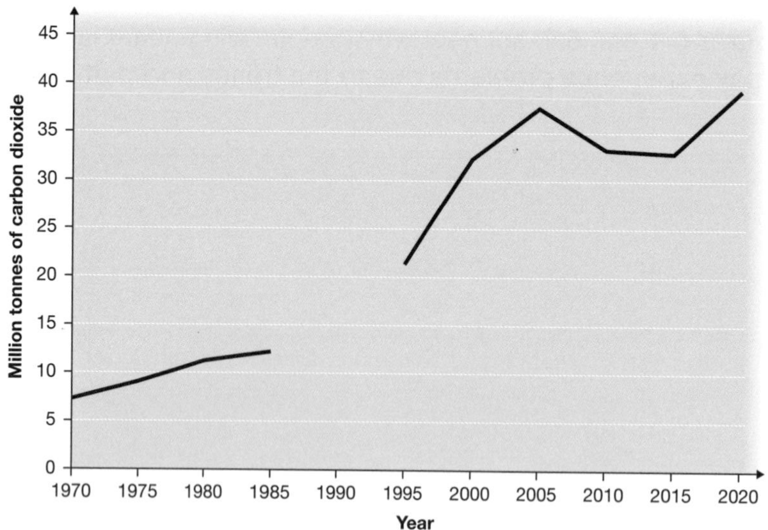

Figure 4

3.1 Using **Figure 4,** complete the graph using the following data for carbon dioxide emissions in 1990.

Million tonnes of carbon dioxide emissions in 1990 = **17.0**

[1 mark]

Study **Figure 5.1**, 'A 1: 50 000 Ordnance Survey map extract of the Heathrow airport area', in the resources (page 99).

3.2 Which **one** of the following six-figure grid references is correct for the bus station in the middle of Heathrow airport?

Shade **one** circle only.

A 050759 ◯

B 073759 ◯

C 075758 ◯

D 085768 ◯

[1 mark]

Study **Figure 5.1**, the OS map extract of the Heathrow airport area.

3.3 Suggest **two** reasons why Heathrow is a suitable site for a major UK airport.

Reason 1: ....

....

Reason 2: ....

....

[2 marks]

Study **Figure 5**, 'Challenges arising from the trends and patterns in UK air traffic', in the resources (pages 99–100).

3.4 **Using Figures 5.1 and 5.2, suggest why people living near Gatwick and Heathrow airports may experience problems due to the trends and patterns in UK air traffic.**

....

....

....

....

....

....

....

....

....

....

....

[6 marks]

Study **Figure 6**, 'Possible solutions to the South-East airport capacity problem', in the resources (page 101).

3.5 **Three possible locations for expanding the South-East airport capacity have been suggested – Heathrow, Gatwick and the Thames Hub. These are explained in Figure 6.**

Which one of these three locations do you think will be the most beneficial for the South-East and the UK as a whole?

Use evidence from the resources booklet and your own understanding to explain why you have reached this decision.

[9 marks + 3 SPaG marks]

Use a separate sheet of paper to write your answer to this question. State your chosen location at the start of your answer.

Paper 3 Section B: Fieldwork

Answer all questions in this section.

Study **Figure 7**, a photograph of part of Slough, Berkshire, and **Figure 8**, a photograph of part of the town of Windsor, Berkshire.

Figure 7 Part of Slough, Berkshire

Figure 8 Part of the town of Windsor, Berkshire

4.1 **A student was investigating the contrasting deprivation levels in Slough and Windsor. Suggest a possible question for their geographical enquiry.**

....

....

[1 mark]

Figure 9 shows data collected from a five-minute traffic count at four different locations in Slough and Windsor.

Slough	
Location 1	92
Location 2	160

Windsor	
Location 3	55
Location 4	15

Figure 9

4.2 **Describe one of the possible risks of carrying out a traffic count survey.**

....

....

[1 mark]

4.3 State **one** reason why the traffic count data may not be accurate.

....

....

[1 mark]

Figure 10 is a bar chart showing the results from the traffic count.

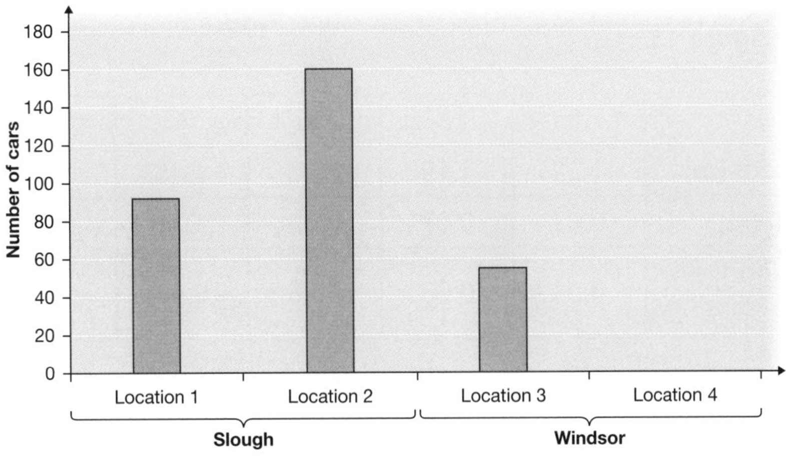

Figure 10

4.4 Complete the bar chart for Location 4 in Windsor on **Figure 10.**

[1 mark]

4.5 Compare the results of the traffic counts for Slough and Windsor.

....

....

....

....

[2 marks]

4.6 Suggest reasons for the results of the traffic counts for Slough and Windsor.

....

....

....

....

[2 marks]

As part of an enquiry collecting primary physical geography data, a student measured the width and depth of the River Horner in Somerset at six different sites, working downstream.

The results are shown in **Figure 11**.

Site	1	2	3	4	5	6
Channel width (m)	1.22	1.19	3.28	4.45	5.08	8.01
Mean depth (m)	0.03	0.07	0.08	0.1	0.22	0.17
Cross-sectional area (m^2)	0.04	0.08	0.26	0.45	1.12	

Figure 11

The cross-sectional area of a river is calculated using the following formula:

channel width × mean depth = cross-sectional area

4.7 Using the data in **Figure 11**, calculate the cross-sectional area of the River Horner for Site 6.

Show your working in the space below.

....

....

....

[2 marks]

4.8 Complete the scatter graph below using the data for the cross-sectional area for Site 6.

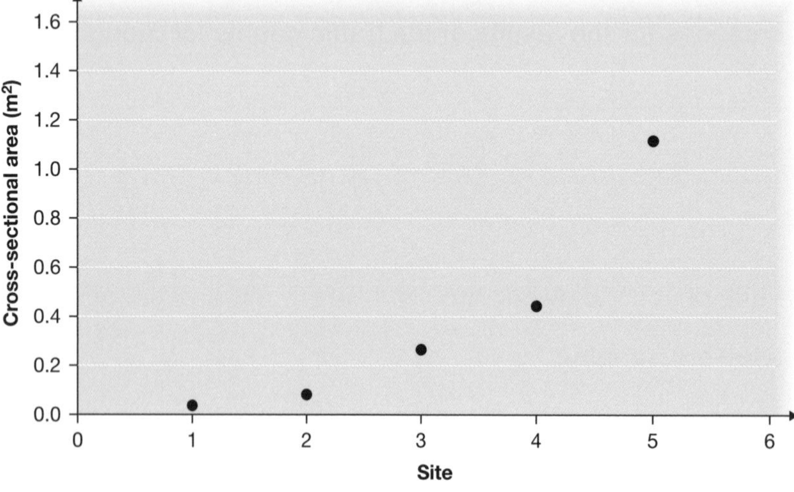

Figure 12

[1 mark]

4.9 Describe **one** of the possible risks of measuring the depth of a river.

....

....

[1 mark]

4.10 Describe the cross-sectional data shown on the scatter graph in **Figure 12.**

....

....

....

....

....

....

[4 marks]

5.1 State the title of your fieldwork enquiry in which **human** geography data was collected.

Title of fieldwork enquiry:

....

Describe **one** of the primary data collection methods used for your fieldwork enquiry.

....

....

....

[2 marks]

5.2 Explain how you presented the primary data that you collected for your human geography fieldwork.

....

....

....

....

[3 marks]

5.3 State the title of your fieldwork enquiry in which physical geography data was collected.

Title of fieldwork enquiry:

....

On a separate sheet of paper assess how successful your primary data collection was in helping you complete your fieldwork enquiry.

[6 marks]

5.4 For **one** of your geography enquiries, explain the results and conclusions of your investigation.

[9 marks + 3 SPaG marks]

Use a separate sheet of paper to write your answer to this question.

Answers

The challenge of natural hazards: Tectonic hazards		
Question	**Marking guidance**	**Total marks**
1	Two points made: • earthquakes are found along plate boundaries • for example, close to the western edge of the South American plate.	2
2	One mark for a reason and the second mark for an extension. • Earthquakes happen where tectonic plates meet. • For example, a destructive plate boundary, where an oceanic plate is subducted underneath a continental plate.	2
3	**Indicative content** • The focus of the question must be on volcanoes at destructive plate margins. • A destructive plate margin is where two plates are moving towards each other. • The denser oceanic plate is subducted beneath the lighter continental plate. • As the oceanic plate moves downwards it melts due to friction and heat from the mantle. • Less dense magma is created which breaks through to the surface to form steep-sided composite volcanoes. • The volcanic eruptions are often very violent and explosive. **Level 2 (Clear) 3–4 marks:** • AO2 Shows clear geographical understanding of why volcanoes occur at destructive plate boundaries. • AO3 Demonstrates application of knowledge and understanding to make full interpretation of the processes which cause volcanoes to occur at destructive plate boundaries. **Level 1 (Basic) 1–2 marks:** • AO2 Shows limited geographical understanding of why volcanoes occur at destructive plate boundaries. • AO3 Demonstrates application of knowledge and understanding to make limited interpretations of the processes which cause volcanoes to occur at destructive plate boundaries. • 0 marks: No relevant content.	4
3	**Indicative content** • Buildings and bridges can be constructed to resist the ground shaking associated with an earthquake. • Walls can be reinforced with steel and concrete to reduce movement. • Shock absorbers can absorb ground shaking. • There are open areas where people go for easy evacuation. • Automatic shutters can come down over windows to prevent broken glass falling. • Rolling weights on a roof can counteract seismic/shock waves. **Level 2 (Clear) 3–4 marks:** • AO1 Demonstrates detailed knowledge of how people can be protected from earthquakes. • AO2 Shows clear geographical understanding of why people need to be protected from earthquakes. **Level 1 (Basic) 1–2 marks:** • AO1 Demonstrates knowledge of how people can be protected from earthquakes. • AO2 Shows some geographical understanding of why people need to be protected from earthquakes. • 0 marks: No relevant content.	4
4	**Indicative content** • Primary effects: number of people killed/injured; buildings destroyed, e.g. schools and hospitals; homelessness; electricity, water supplies, sanitation and communications affected; need for food and shelter. • Secondary effects: landslides; flooding; spread of disease, e.g. cholera; tsunami; fires. • Named example: should be both place and date specific, e.g. the L'Aquila earthquake in central Italy on 6 April 2009. **Level 3 (Detailed) 5–6 marks:** • AO3 Demonstrates thorough application of knowledge and understanding to give detailed description of earthquakes. Includes detailed place-specific information. • AO3 Shows full understanding of the interrelationships between primary and secondary effects, using evidence to support response. **Level 2 (Clear) 3–4 marks:** • AO1 Demonstrates specific and accurate knowledge of the effects of an earthquake. Includes place-specific information. • AO2 Shows clear geographical understanding of primary and secondary effects. **Level 1 (Basic) 1–2 marks:** • AO1 Demonstrates some knowledge of the effects of earthquakes. May include some place-specific information. • AO2 Shows limited geographical understanding of difference between primary and secondary effects. • 0 marks: No relevant content.	6

The challenge of natural hazards: Weather hazards		
Question	**Marking guidance**	**Total marks**
1	One mark for each correct answer: **B** Tropical storms form above warm oceans (27°C or above). **D** The conditions in the eye of the storm are calm. No credit if three or more statements are shaded.	2
2	One mark for a reason and the second mark for an extension: • a large number of people die by drowning in a storm surge • people are made homeless due to strong winds damaging homes.	2
3	**Indicative content** • Windows, doors and roofs reinforced to strengthen buildings to withstand strong winds. • Houses constructed on stilts so that a storm surge will pass beneath. • Storm shelters built. • Educating people to be prepared for tropical storms. **Level 2 (Clear) 3–4 marks:** • AO1 Demonstrates detailed knowledge of how people can prepare for tropical storms. • AO2 Shows clear geographical understanding of why people need to prepare for tropical storms. **Level 1 (Basic) 1–2 marks:** • AO1 Demonstrates knowledge of how people can prepare for tropical storms. • AO2 Shows some geographical understanding of why people need to prepare for tropical storms. • 0 marks: No relevant content.	4

<table>
<tr>
<td>4</td>
<td>
Indicative content
• Primary effects: number of people killed; people displaced/homeless; homes destroyed; buildings destroyed, e.g. schools and hospitals; communications/transport links interrupted and/or destroyed; fishing boats destroyed; crops destroyed; flooding.
• Secondary effects: loss of jobs and income; flooding causes landslides, cutting off roads; power supplies cut off; shortages of water, food and shelter, which can lead to outbreaks of disease; education disrupted after schools are destroyed; looting of shops.
• Named example: should be both place and date specific, e.g. Typhoon Haiyan, Philippines, 2013.
Level 3 (Detailed) 7–9 marks:
• A01 Demonstrates detailed knowledge of the primary and secondary effects of a tropical storm.
• A02 Shows thorough geographical understanding of the interrelationships between places, environments and processes in the context of tropical storms.
• A03 Demonstrates application of knowledge and understanding in an effective and reasoned way in assessing the significance of effects.
Level 2 (Clear) 4–6 marks:
• A01 Demonstrates clear knowledge of the primary and secondary effects of a tropical storm.
• A02 Shows some geographical understanding of the interrelationships between places, environments and processes in the context of tropical storms.
• A03 Demonstrates reasonable application of knowledge and understanding in assessing the significance of effects.
Level 1 (Basic) 1–3 marks:
• A01 Demonstrates limited knowledge of the primary and secondary effects of a tropical storm.
• A02 Shows slight understanding of the interrelationships between places, environments and processes in the context of tropical storms.
• A03 Demonstrates limited application of knowledge and understanding in assessing the significance of effects.
• 0 marks: No relevant content.
<table>
<tr><th colspan="3">Spelling, punctuation and grammar</th></tr>
<tr><td>High performance</td><td>3 marks</td><td>• Spelling and punctuation are consistently accurate.
• Answers use rules of grammar with effective overall control of meaning.
• Answers use a wide range of specialist terms as appropriate.</td></tr>
<tr><td>Intermediate performance</td><td>2 marks</td><td>• Spelling and punctuation are generally accurate.
• Answers use rules of grammar with general overall control of meaning.
• Answers use a good range of specialist terms as appropriate.</td></tr>
<tr><td>Threshold performance</td><td>1 mark</td><td>• Spelling and punctuation are reasonably accurate.
• Answers use rules of grammar with some control of meaning and any errors do not significantly hinder meaning overall.
• Answers use a limited range of specialist terms as appropriate.</td></tr>
<tr><td>Below threshold performance</td><td>0 marks</td><td>• Nothing is written.
• The answer does not relate to the question.
• The answer SPaG does not reach the threshold performance level, for example, errors in spelling, punctuation and grammar severely hinder meaning.</td></tr>
</table>
</td>
<td>9+3 SPaG</td>
</tr>
<tr>
<td>5</td>
<td>
Indicative content
Social examples, such as:
• houses flooded
• residents evacuated and put into temporary shelters
• farms evacuated
• daily routine affected – going to work, school, etc.
• power supplies cut off.
Economic examples, such as:
• cost of flood damage
• agricultural land affected
• livestock evacuated
• local roads cut off affecting people's journeys to work
• railway lines affected.
Environmental examples, such as:
• floodwaters contaminated with sewage and other pollutants
• debris deposited which had to be cleared
• stagnant water – had to be reoxygenated before putting back into a river.
• Named example: should be both place and date specific, e.g. the Somerset floods of January 2014.
Level 3 (Detailed) 5–6 marks:
• A01 Demonstrates detailed knowledge of the impacts of a flood on the people and environment.
• A02 Shows thorough geographical understanding of the interrelationship between places, environments and processes in the context of flooding.
• A03 Demonstrates application of knowledge and understanding in assessing the significance of the impacts.
Level 2 (Clear) 3–4 marks:
• A01 Demonstrates clear knowledge of the impacts of a flood on the people and environment.
• A02 Shows some geographical understanding of the interrelationship between places, environments and processes in the context of flooding.
• A03 Demonstrates reasonable application of knowledge and understanding in assessing the significance of the impacts.
Level 1 (Basic) 1–2 marks:
• A01 Demonstrates limited knowledge of the impacts of a flood on the people and environment.
• A02 Shows slight geographical understanding of the interrelationship between places, environments and processes in the context of flooding.
• A03 Demonstrates limited application of knowledge and understanding in assessing the significance of the impacts.
• 0 marks: No relevant content.
</td>
<td>6</td>
</tr>
<tr>
<td>6</td>
<td>
Indicative content
• Answers should include a judgement to the extent they agree with the statement, so answer should provide evidence for and against the statement. Answers must relate to the UK.
• More energy in the atmosphere could lead to more intense storms.
• The atmospheric circulation could be affected, bringing more floods to normally dry regions and heat waves to normally cooler areas.
• No single weather event can be blamed on climate change.
• Evidence to support more extreme weather – 2013/14 and 2015/16 heavy rainfall causing devastating floods; 2009 and 2010 heavy snowfall.
Level 3 (Detailed) 7–9 marks:
• A01 Demonstrates comprehensive knowledge of how the weather in the UK may change.
• A02 Shows thorough geographical understanding of the interrelationships between places, environments and processes in the context of the UK's weather.
• A03 Demonstrates thorough application of knowledge and understanding in evaluating the extent to which the UK's weather is becoming more extreme.
Level 2 (Clear) 4–6 marks:
• A01 Demonstrates clear knowledge of how the weather in the UK may change.
• A02 Shows some geographical understanding of the interrelationships between places, environments and processes in the context of the UK's weather.
• A03 Demonstrates reasonable application of knowledge and understanding in evaluating the extent to which the UK's weather is becoming more extreme.
Level 1 (Basic) 1–3 marks:
• A01 Demonstrates limited knowledge of how the weather in the UK may change.
• A02 Shows slight understanding of the interrelationships between places, environments and processes in the context of the UK's weather.
• A03 Demonstrates limited application of knowledge and understanding in evaluating the extent to which the UK's weather is becoming more extreme.
• 0 marks: No relevant content.
For SPaG marks, please see table above.
</td>
<td>9+3 SPaG</td>
</tr>
</table>

The challenge of natural hazards: Climate change		
Question	Marking guidance	Total marks
1	One mark for a reason and the second mark for an extension: volcanic ash can block out sunlight. This leads to a reduction in temperatures in the short term.	2
2	One mark each for two of the following: alternative energy sources, carbon capture, planting trees, international agreements.	2
3	**Indicative content** • The enhanced greenhouse effect is the impact caused by the heat retained in the atmosphere by the greenhouse gases added to the atmosphere through human activity. • More carbon dioxide has been added to the atmosphere through burning fossil fuels, increased transportation and deforestation. • Methane has been added to the atmosphere through more intense farming, such as rice farming and cattle ranching. **Level 2 (Clear) 3–4 marks:** • A01 Demonstrates detailed knowledge of the enhanced greenhouse effect. • A02 Shows clear geographical understanding of what causes the enhanced greenhouse effect. **Level 1 (Basic) 1–2 marks:** • A01 Demonstrates knowledge of the enhanced greenhouse effect. • A02 Shows some geographical understanding of what causes the enhanced greenhouse effect. • 0 marks: No relevant content.	4
4	**Indicative content** • Natural causes of climate change are orbital changes such as eccentricity, which causes changes in the elliptical path of the Sun, affecting the temperature of the Earth. • Increase in solar energy linked to sunspots: the more sunspots there are the more solar radiation is given out. • Volcanic ash can block out sunlight and so temperatures are reduced. • Sulfur dioxide from a volcanic eruption mixes with water to cause sulfuric acid. This reflects the Sun's radiation, reducing temperatures. **Level 2 (Clear) 3–4 marks:** • A01 Demonstrates detailed knowledge of natural causes of climate change. • A02 Shows clear geographical understanding of what causes natural climate change. **Level 1 (Basic) 1–2 marks:** • A01 Demonstrates knowledge of natural causes of climate change. • A02 Shows some geographical understanding of what causes natural climate change. • 0 marks: No relevant content.	4
5	**Indicative content** • Burning fossil fuels is the largest contributor to climate change. • Fossil fuels are used in transport, industry and power stations to generate electricity. • Intensive agriculture has contributed to an increase in methane due to cattle and rice farming. • Forests act as carbon stores. Deforestation has reduced the number of trees. This means more carbon dioxide is released into the atmosphere. **Level 3 (Detailed) 5–6 marks:** • A01 Demonstrates detailed knowledge of how humans have contributed to climate change. • A02 Shows thorough geographical understanding of the interrelationship between places, environments and processes in the context of climate change. **Level 2 (Clear) 3–4 marks:** • A01 Demonstrates clear knowledge of how humans have contributed to climate change. • A02 Shows some geographical understanding of the interrelationship between places, environments and processes in the context of climate change. **Level 1 (Basic) 1–2 marks:** • A01 Demonstrates limited knowledge of how humans have contributed to climate change. • A02 Shows slight geographical understanding of the interrelationship between places, environments and processes in the context of climate change. • 0 marks: No relevant content.	6

The living world: Ecosystems		
Question	Marking guidance	Total marks
1	One mark for the correct answer: **C** Soils get nutrients from the decomposition of litter. No credit if two or more statements are shaded.	1
2	Credit statements about what water does in the nutrient cycle using information in the diagram, such as: • washing of nutrients deep into a soil (leaching) (1) • rain runs over the ground and carries nutrients away (1) • rain supplies some dissolved nutrients (1) • moisture helps the decomposition process (1) • water dissolves nutrients so that plants can absorb them through their roots (1). No credit for simply listing parts of the water or nutrient cycles.	2
3	One mark for the correct answer: **C** Large temperature range during a year (–250°C to +100°C) and low precipitation (approximately 500 mm a year). No credit if two or more statements are shaded.	1
4	**Indicative content** • Responses should include description and explanation. • There should be evidence that the candidate knows the small-scale ecosystem, e.g. types of flora and fauna, soil and climate. • Links should be clear and specific, showing understanding of food webs, nutrient cycling and other processes. • Max level 1 for either description or explanation. **Level 3 (Detailed) 5–6 marks:** • A01 Applies detailed knowledge of small-scale UK ecosystem to interpret the question. • A03 Clearly relates characteristics of the ecosystem to links. **Level 2 (Clear) 3–4 marks:** • A01 Demonstrates accurate knowledge of the features of vegetation, climate and other natural factors to support the explanation. • A03 Relates some characteristics of the ecosystem to links. • A04 Makes effective use of diagrams. **Level 1 (Basic) 1–2 marks:** • A01 Demonstrates limited knowledge of vegetation, climate and other natural factors in UK ecosystem. • A04 Makes no use of visual material. • 0 marks: No relevant content.	6

5	**Indicative content** • Responses should include description *and* explanation. • There should be evidence that the candidate knows the small-scale ecosystem, e.g. the links between different parts and between factors influencing change. • Climate/weather extremes causing change. • Human management of the ecosystem. • Conflict between nature and specified human activities or presence. • Max level 1 for either description or explanation. **Level 3 (Detailed) 5–6 marks:** • AO1 Applies detailed knowledge of small-scale UK ecosystem to interpret the question. • AO3 Clearly relates characteristic(s) of the ecosystem to factors affecting the natural balance. **Level 2 (Clear) 3–4 marks:** • AO1 Demonstrates accurate knowledge of the features of the UK ecosystem to support the explanation. • AO4 Makes clear and effective use of diagrams. **Level 1 (Basic) 1–2 marks:** • AO1 Demonstrates limited knowledge of the UK ecosystem and the balance within it. • AO4 Makes limited use visual material • 0 marks: No relevant content.	6
6	**Indicative content for tropical rainforests, hot deserts and/or cold environments (as appropriate)** • The question requires consideration of the extent to which the interactions between the living and non-living parts of two global ecosystems create a balance in the ecosystem. • Answers may describe the balance that exists in two or more global ecosystems. • Answers may focus on specific examples within generalisations such as climate, which determines plant growth (producers) at the base of trophic levels through heat, rain and sunlight; soils providing nutrients for plant growth and humus being added by plants (nutrient cycle); the supply of water for plants and animals. • Answers may consider factors that upset the balance such as climate change and human actions. • Answers must consider natural processes. **Level 3 (Detailed) 7–9 marks:** • AO1 Demonstrates comprehensive and accurate knowledge of locations, places and processes in relation to tropical rainforests, hot deserts and/or cold environments. • AO2 Shows thorough geographical understanding of the interrelationships between places, environments and processes in the context of tropical rainforests, hot deserts and/or cold environments. • AO3 Demonstrates thorough application of knowledge and understanding in evaluating the extent to which interactions between biotic and abiotic parts create balance in tropical rainforests, hot deserts and/or cold environments. **Level 2 (Clear) 4–6 marks:** • AO1 Demonstrates clear knowledge of locations, places and processes in relation to tropical rainforests, hot deserts and/or cold environments. • AO2 Shows some geographical understanding of the interrelationships between places, environments and processes in the context of tropical rainforests, hot deserts and/or cold environments. • AO3 Demonstrates reasonable application of knowledge and understanding in evaluating the extent to which interactions between biotic and abiotic parts create balance in tropical rainforests, hot deserts and/or cold environments. **Level 1 (Basic) 1–3 marks:** • AO1 Demonstrates limited knowledge of locations, places and processes in relation to tropical rainforests, hot deserts and/or cold environments. • AO2 Shows slight geographical understanding of the interrelationships between places, environments and processes in the context of tropical rainforests, hot deserts and/or cold environments. • AO3 Demonstrates limited application of knowledge and understanding in evaluating the extent to which interactions between biotic and abiotic parts create balance in tropical rainforests, hot deserts and/or cold environments. • 0 marks: No relevant content. **For SPaG marks, please see table in Weather hazards section.**	9+3 SPaG

The living world: Tropical rainforests		
Question	**Marking guidance**	**Total marks**
1	One mark for the correct answer: **D** Nutrient cycling is very fast. No credit if two or more statements are shaded.	1
2	**Indicative content** • An area of tropical rainforest must be identified. • Responses should include description *and* explanation. • There should be evidence that the candidate knows the global ecosystem and what has been happening to it. • Causes such as: LIC/NEEs trying to make money to help development; businesses trying to make money; poor people trying to improve their lives; country trying to use resources. • Max level 1 for either description or explanation. **Level 3 (Detailed) 5–6 marks:** • AO1 Applies detailed knowledge of a tropical rainforest to interpret the question. • AO3 Clearly relates a description of deforestation to reasons for the deforestation. **Level 2 (Clear) 3–4 marks:** • AO1 Demonstrates accurate knowledge of the features of deforestation to support the explanation. • AO4 Makes clear and effective use of photograph. **Level 1 (Basic) 1–2 marks:** • AO1 Demonstrates limited knowledge of deforestation in a tropical rainforest. • AO4 Makes limited use visual material. • 0 marks: No relevant content.	6
3	One mark for the correct answer: French Guiana. No credit for Guyana or any other country.	1
4	One mark for the correct answer: Four/4 (countries).	1

5	Credit one value only. Value must be to people, not to the natural environment. One mark for stating a value, such as: • source of valuable resources (1) • place to live and make a living (1) • provision of oxygen (1) • store carbon (1) • biodiversity (1). Second mark for a developed explanation. • Resources in the forest such as foods, timber, medicines or under the forest, such as coal, oil, metals, can be used to provide jobs and make money for people and countries (1). • As populations grow, people need living space and ways of farming to get their own food or products to sell (1). • People need oxygen to breathe, which is produced by plants and the greatest number of trees is in the tropical rainforest (1). • Climate change is and will continue to greatly affect people; the tropical rainforest stores carbon and stops some CO_2 getting into the atmosphere to create more warming (1). • The huge biodiversity provides chemicals and substances which people may be able to use to create medicines and other beneficial products (1).	2
6	Credit one impact only. The answer must focus on a negative impact of deforestation of a tropical rainforest and should be referenced to one area (e.g. Malaysia or South-East Asian rainforest). One mark for stating a negative impact, such as: • reduction of biodiversity (1) • erosion of soils (1) • increased rate of climate change (1) • local area becomes drier (1) or may lead to increased flooding (1) • water and air pollution increase (1) • reduction of eco-tourism (1) Second mark for a developed explanation. • If biodiversity is reduced, the wildlife may be made extinct, creating a loss of a resource to nature (food web unbalanced) and people (source of medicine) (1). • Erosion and degradation of soils means that the forest or crops will not grow and natural resources will be lost (1). • Climate change threatens natural ecosystems by making them hotter or drier, which then reduces resources to support people (1). • Drier climate damages trees and causes dieback and further forest loss (1). • Pollution damages the conditions in which trees and plants live and also the health of people (1). • A damaged forest does not appeal to people for their holidays and so tourism income is lost (1).	2
7	Credit one way only. The answer must focus on education of people and sustainability of the tropical rainforest. One mark for stating an aspect of education, such as: • value of the tropical rainforest (1) • ways of looking after tropical rainforest (1) • rates and types of damage (1) • ways of reducing damage to tropical rainforest (1) • alternative ways of making money (1). Second mark for a developed explanation. • If people appreciate the need for biodiversity and the benefits from tropical rainforest products, they are less likely to cut them down (1). • Understanding of the role of national parks, biosphere reserves and nature reserves so that their designation is recognised by people (1). • Understanding of the rapid loss and the consequences for local people, countries and the world would make people appreciate the need to look after tropical rainforests (1). • Sustainable logging practices, agroforestry rather than clearance and shifting cultivation help maintain forest structure and biodiversity (1). • Instead of cutting down tropical rainforests for money, things like eco-tourism can provide income based on an undamaged tropical rainforest (1).	2
8	**Indicative content for tropical rainforests (as appropriate)** • The question requires consideration of the extent to which the ecosystem provides opportunities and challenges for development. • Answers must focus on both opportunities and challenges. Opportunities such as: providing a range of resources, which can be used to provide jobs and money, including exports; providing living space for poorer people to help improve their quality of life; providing opportunities for agroforestry to provide food and export crops. Challenges such as: soils are infertile; resources difficult to access; some resources, such as medical compounds, are undiscovered; a very complex ecosystem, which makes it difficult to assess impacts of human activities; reducing loss of biodiversity; preventing changes to climate balance. • Must indicate, through reference to specific examples, the balance between opportunities and challenges. **Level 3 (Detailed) 7–9 marks:** • AO1 Demonstrates comprehensive and accurate knowledge of locations, places and processes in relation to a tropical rainforest. • AO2 Shows thorough geographical understanding of the interrelationships between places, environments and processes in the context of a tropical rainforest. • AO3 Demonstrates thorough application of knowledge and understanding in evaluating the extent to which the ecosystem provides opportunities and challenges for development. **Level 2 (Clear) 4–6 marks:** • AO1 Demonstrates clear knowledge of locations, places and processes in relation to a tropical rainforest. • AO2 Shows some geographical understanding of the interrelationships between places, environments and processes in the context of a tropical rainforest. • AO3 Demonstrates reasonable application of knowledge and understanding in evaluating the extent to which the ecosystem provides opportunities and challenges for development. **Level 1 (Basic) 1–3 marks:** • AO1 Demonstrates limited knowledge of locations, places and processes in relation to a tropical rainforest. • AO2 Shows slight geographical understanding of the interrelationships between places, environments and processes in the context of a tropical rainforest. • AO3 Demonstrates limited application of knowledge and understanding in evaluating the extent to which the ecosystem provides opportunities and challenges for development. • 0 marks: No relevant content. **For SPaG marks, please see table in Weather hazards section.**	9+3 SPaG

The living world: Hot deserts		
Question	**Marking guidance**	**Total marks**
1	One mark for the correct answer: **C** 29°C No credit if two or more statements are shaded.	1
2	One mark for the correct answer: 7 mm. (Units must be given.)	1
3	Credit statements about causes of desertification, such as: • climate has changed to be drier in some semi-arid areas (1) • overpopulation has led to cutting down too many trees for fuel and using up too much water (1) • overgrazing by livestock has removed grasses that held soil together (1) • higher evaporation rates has removed moisture from soils allowing it to be blown away (1) No credit for simply defining desertification or describing what the area is like.	2

4	**Indicative content** • Using fences (e.g. brushwood) as windbreaks (1) to slow the movement of sand into semi-arid areas (1). • Terracing fields and slopes (1) so that any rain has time to soak into soils rather than running away (1). • Creating furrows across fields so that any rainwater is trapped and has time to soak into the soils (1). • Plant drought-resistant trees (1) so that they hold soil together, shelter it from wind and shade the land so that evaporation is reduced (1). **Level 2 (Clear) 3–4 marks:** • AO3 Demonstrates accurate interpretation of desertification through the application of relevant understanding and knowledge. **Level 1 (Basic) 1–2 marks:** • AO3 Demonstrates some interpretation of desertification through the limited application of relevant understanding and knowledge. • 0 marks: No relevant content.	4
5	**Indicative content** • The lack of water means that even plants that have adapted find it difficult to survive (1) as shown by the dead trees in Figure 6 (1). • Any water or lakes that form may evaporate quickly (1) as shown by the cracked ground in the photo (1). • It is often dry for long periods of time with clear skies (as shown in Figure 6) (1) so plants and animals have difficulty finding shade (1). **Level 2 (Clear) 3–4 marks:** • AO3 Demonstrates accurate explanation of hot desert ecosystem vulnerability through the application of relevant knowledge and understanding. • AO4 Makes clear and effective use of the image to support the explanation of vulnerability. **Level 1 (Basic) 1–2 marks:** • AO3 Demonstrates some explanation of hot desert ecosystem vulnerability through the application of limited relevant knowledge and understanding. • AO4 Makes limited use of the image to support the explanation of vulnerability.	4
6	**Indicative content** Responses must include description **and** explanation. There should be evidence that the candidate knows a hot desert ecosystem. Links should be clear and specific, showing understanding of importance, such as: • delicate balance in a fragile environment so links could be easily broken • many animals are nocturnal because that is when it is cooler • plants are adapted to store water when available or have long roots to get to groundwater because there is little rain • plants and insects have adapted their growth cycles to be fast when rain does occur • soils lack nutrients so plants only grow slowly • oases are places of greater biodiversity due to the water supply. Max level 1 for either description or explanation. **Level 3 (Detailed) 5–6 marks:** • AO1 Applies detailed knowledge of a hot desert ecosystem to interpret the question. • AO3 Clearly relates characteristic(s) of the ecosystem to links and their importance. **Level 2 (Clear) 3–4 marks:** • AO1 Demonstrates accurate knowledge of how the links between animals, vegetation, climate and other natural factors are important. • AO4 Makes effective use of diagrams. **Level 1 (Basic) 1–2 marks:** • AO1 Demonstrates limited knowledge of how animals, vegetation, climate and other natural factors are important. • AO4 Makes no use of diagrams. • 0 marks: No relevant content.	6
7	**Indicative content** The hot desert environment should be stated. In the accompanying AQA GCSE Geography Revision Guide, this is the Thar Desert. The question requires consideration of the extent to which opportunities are greater than the challenges for development; a candidate may decide that they are not greater. Answers must focus on both opportunities and challenges and compare them. Example opportunities are: • extracting valuable minerals (such as gypsum, marble, lignite and oil), which help energy security and give industries materials they can use • clear skies for developing solar energy and strong winds for wind energy – renewable resources providing electricity for people • desert festivals attracting tourist income • large quantities of different crops can be grown once irrigation water is provided. Example challenges are: • extreme heat during the day and in summer making it difficult to work • high evaporation rates contaminating fields with salts (salinisation) and causing large water losses from irrigation canals • population growth placing greater and greater demands on the water supply situation • transport infrastructure is difficult to maintain because of heat and moving sand. Must indicate, through reference to specific examples, whether the opportunities are greater than the challenges or not. **Level 3 (Detailed) 7–9 marks:** • AO1 Demonstrates comprehensive and accurate knowledge of locations, places and processes in relation to a hot desert environment. • AO2 Shows thorough geographical understanding of the interrelationships between places, environments and processes in the context of a hot desert environment. • AO3 Demonstrates thorough application of knowledge and understanding in evaluating the extent to which the opportunities are greater than the challenges for development. **Level 2 (Clear) 4–6 marks:** • AO1 Demonstrates clear knowledge of locations, places and processes in relation to a hot desert environment. • AO2 Shows some geographical understanding of the interrelationships between places, environments and processes in the context of a hot desert environment. • AO3 Demonstrates reasonable application of knowledge and understanding in evaluating the extent to which opportunities are greater than the challenges for development. **Level 1 (Basic) 1–3 marks:** • AO1 Demonstrates limited knowledge of locations, places and processes in relation to a hot desert environment. • AO2 Shows slight geographical understanding of the interrelationships between places, environments and processes in the context of a hot desert environment. • AO3 Demonstrates limited application of knowledge and understanding in evaluating the extent to which opportunities are greater than the challenges for development. • 0 marks: No relevant content. **For SPaG marks, please see table in Weather hazards section.**	9+3 SPaG

The living world: Cold environments		
Question	**Marking guidance**	**Total marks**
1	One mark for the correct answer: **D** –9.9°C No! If the temperature is taken as the middle of December column, then the average temp is –11.5°C No credit if two or more statements are shaded AO4 = 1 mark	1
2	One mark for the correct answer: 20 mm. (Units must be given.)	1

3	Credit statements about adaptations to the cold or dry conditions, such as: • rapid plant growth in short summer (1) • plants grow low to ground to avoid wind-chill effect (1) • white camouflage used by herbivores and carnivores to avoid being spotted against the snow (1) • caribou have wide hooves to avoid sinking into waterlogged ground (1) • many animals have layers of fur or fat to keep warm (1). No credit for simple listing, candidates must outline.	2
4	**Indicative content** • The lack of liquid water for part of a year means that even plants that have adapted find it difficult to survive (1) as shown by the bare patches of ground in Figure 8 (1). • Snow and ice can cover the ground for a long time making it difficult for plants to grow through (1) as shown by the large patch of snow in the photo (1). • The cold conditions are made worse by wind chill so plants have to grow close to the ground to survive (1) as shown by the low plants in the foreground of Figure 8 and the absence of trees (1). **Level 2 (Clear) 3–4 marks:** • A03 Demonstrates accurate explanation of cold environment ecosystem vulnerability through the application of relevant knowledge and understanding. • A04 Makes clear and effective use of the image to support the explanation of vulnerability. **Level 1 (Basic) 1–2 marks:** • A03 Demonstrates some explanation of cold environment ecosystem vulnerability through the application of limited relevant knowledge and understanding. • A04 Makes limited use of the image to support the explanation of vulnerability.	4
5	One mark for each suggestion (up to a maximum of two) that shows understanding of the benefits of cold wilderness areas for people, such as: • genetic diversity for scientific study that may give future medicines • training areas for isolation in space exploration • past and present climate change information from ice cores in Antarctica, etc. • provides comparison with areas that have been damaged by human activities. No credit for vague statements such as 'see animals' or 'go on holiday to'.	2
6	**Indicative content** Responses must include description and explanation. There should be evidence that the candidate knows cold environment locations. Methods should be clear and specific, showing understanding, such as: • design oil pipelines to withstand the climate conditions and the permafrost (e.g. the Alaskan pipeline) • establish nature reserves or national parks to protect areas (e.g. Arctic National Wildlife Reserve in Alaska, USA) • obey international treaties established to protect areas and wildlife (e.g. Antarctic Treaty and ban on whaling) • develop new international agreements to protect areas (e.g. in the Arctic). Max level 1 for either description or explanation. **Level 3 (Detailed) 5–6 marks:** • A01 Applies detailed knowledge of a cold environment to interpret the question. • A03 Clearly relates problems of economic development to how they can be reduced. **Level 2 (Clear) 3–4 marks:** • A01 Demonstrates accurate knowledge of a cold environment and links it to problems of economic development. • A03 Makes effective use of understanding of how to reduce problems. **Level 1 (Basic) 1–2 marks:** • A01 Demonstrates limited knowledge of a cold environment that has experienced economic development. • A03 Makes no reference to solving or reducing problems. • 0 marks: No relevant content.	6
7	**Indicative content** The question requires consideration of the extent to which climate determines the characteristics of a cold environment ecosystem. The answer must indicate, through reference to specific examples, how the natural environment is affected by climate and suggest which other factors may be important. Answers may focus on: • very low temperatures in Antarctica that create an ice sheet so wildlife is only found at the fringes of the continent • animals and plants have to adapt to the cold through having layers of fat or fur to keep warm • the cold temperatures freeze the ground (permafrost) so that it is difficult for plants to grow or animals to get food • widespread snow and ice has encouraged animals to camouflage themselves • plants are small to escape the cold winds • human activities affected by the climate. **Level 3 (Detailed) 7–9 marks:** • A01 Demonstrates comprehensive and accurate knowledge of locations, places and processes in relation to a cold environment. • A02 Shows thorough geographical understanding of the interrelationships between climate and biotic and abiotic parts of a cold environment ecosystem. • A03 Demonstrates thorough application of knowledge and understanding in evaluating the extent to which the ecosystem characteristics result from the climate. **Level 2 (Clear) 4–6 marks:** • A01 Demonstrates clear knowledge of locations, places and processes in relation to a cold environment. • A02 Shows some geographical understanding of the interrelationships between climate and biotic and abiotic parts of a cold environment ecosystem. • A03 Demonstrates reasonable application of knowledge and understanding in evaluating the extent to which the ecosystem characteristics result from the climate. **Level 1 (Basic) 1–3 marks:** • A01 Demonstrates limited knowledge of locations, places and processes in relation to a cold environment. • A02 Shows slight geographical understanding of the interrelationships between climate and biotic and abiotic parts of a cold environment ecosystem. • A03 Demonstrates limited application of knowledge and understanding in evaluating the extent to which the ecosystem characteristics result from climate. • 0 marks: No relevant content. **For SPaG marks, please see table in Weather hazards section.**	9+3 SPaG

Physical landscapes in the UK: Coastal landscapes in the UK		
Question	**Marking guidance**	**Total marks**
1	The feature is a spit.	1
2	The spit is formed by the process of longshore drift.	1
3	B 318897	1

<table>
<tr><td>4</td><td>Indicative content
• Constructive waves are gently sloping whereas destructive waves are steep.
• Constructive waves have a strong swash, which helps to build up beaches whereas destructive waves have a strong backwash, which removes beach material.
• Constructive waves have a long wavelength but destructive waves have a short wavelength.
Level 2 (Clear) 3–4 marks:
• AO2 Shows clear understanding of why constructive and destructive waves are different.
• AO3 Demonstrates application of knowledge and understanding to make full interpretation of the processes that cause constructive and destructive waves.
Level 1 (Basic) 1–2 marks:
• AO2 Shows limited understanding of the difference between constructive and destructive waves.
• AO3 Demonstrates application of knowledge and understanding to make limited interpretations of the processes that cause constructive and destructive waves.
• 0 marks: No relevant content.</td><td>4</td></tr>
<tr><td>5</td><td>Indicative content
• A large crack forms in the headland at a point of weakness.
• The crack is enlarged by the process of hydraulic action and abrasion to form a notch.
• Waves make the crack larger over time to form a cave.
• Two caves form back-to-back over time.
• These will eventually cut through the headland to form an arch.
Level 2 (Clear) 3–4 marks:
• AO2 Shows clear understanding of how an arch is formed.
• AO3 Application is sound with clear interpretation of processes involved.
Level 1 (Basic) 1–2 marks:
• AO2 Shows limited understanding of how an arch is formed.
• AO3 Application is limited with basic interpretation of processes involved.
• 0 marks: No relevant content.</td><td>4</td></tr>
<tr><td>6</td><td>Indicative content
• Process of longshore drift transports material along the coast in a zigzag movement, with the swash bringing material up the beach at a 45-degree angle and then the backwash removing it at a 90-degree angle.
• When there is a change in direction of the coast, such as at a river estuary or headland, the sea loses energy and material is deposited.
• The process is repeated over time and a spit is formed extending out across the estuary.
• A change in wind direction causes the spit to create a hooked or curved end.
• A salt marsh develops behind the spit.
• Other depositional features may also be described – tombolos and bar. These should follow the same ideas about deposition occurring when the sea is calm and has less energy to transport material.
Level 3 (Detailed) 5–6 marks
• AO3 Demonstrates thorough application of knowledge and understanding to give detailed explanations of depositional landforms.
• AO3 Shows full understanding of the interrelationships between coastal environments and processes.
Level 2 (Clear) 3–4 marks:
• AO1 Demonstrates specific and accurate knowledge of depositional processes and the landforms they create along the coast.
• AO2 Shows clear geographical understanding of the interrelationships between coastal environments and processes.
Level 1 (Basic) 1–2 marks:
• AO1 Demonstrates some knowledge of depositional processes. Alternatively, may be descriptive about landform appearance and structure.
• AO2 Shows limited geographical understanding of the interrelationships between coastal environments and processes.
• 0 marks: No relevant content.</td><td>6</td></tr>
</table>

<table>
<tr><th colspan="3">Physical landscapes in the UK: River landscapes in the UK</th></tr>
<tr><th>Question</th><th>Marking guidance</th><th>Total marks</th></tr>
<tr><td>1a</td><td>Lag time is the length of time between the peak rainfall and the river's peak discharge.</td><td>1</td></tr>
<tr><td>1b</td><td>Peak discharge – peak rainfall. 6.8 – 3.5 = 3.3 hours.</td><td>1</td></tr>
<tr><td>2</td><td>Indicative content
Physical factors
• Precipitation – heavy rainfall can lead to flash flooding or a long period of rain can lead to flooding.
• Geology – impermeable rock increases surface run-off, which increases rate of which water reaches a river.
• Saturated soil – waterlogged soil doesn't allow water to infiltrate.
Human factors
• Deforestation – this decreases the amount of interception so rainfall can get to rivers quicker.
• Urbanisation – increased impermeable surfaces which increases speed of which water reaches rivers.</td><td>4</td></tr>
<tr><td>3</td><td>Answers using evidence from the map, including grid references if available:
• Source of River Wye shown in grid square 80;87.
• Upland area shown by the contour lines being close together.
• Peak high ground at 724 m in grid square 81:87.
• Shape of contours formed in a v shape with River Wye at the bottom.</td><td>4</td></tr>
<tr><td>4</td><td>As it runs from source to mouth, the cross-section of a river becomes:
• wider
• deeper.</td><td>2</td></tr>
<tr><td>5</td><td>Indicative content
• There will be larger and more angular sediment in the upper course.
• The sediment will be considerably smaller and rounder in the lower course.
• Sediment will be rounder and smoother as sediment is transported and eroded as it is moved downstream.
• Erosion processes of hydraulic action, attrition and abrasion are key in reducing the size of sediment as it moves downstream.
Level 2 (Clear) 3–4 marks:
• AO2 Shows clear understanding of how and why sediment changes from source to mouth.
• AO3 Application is sound with clear interpretation of processes involved.
Level 1 (Basic) 1–2 marks:
• AO2 Shows limited understanding of how size of sediment changes from source to mouth.
• AO3 Application is limited with basic interpretation of processes involved.
• 0 marks: No relevant content.</td><td>4</td></tr>
</table>

6	**Indicative content** • Floodplains are found in the lower stage, of a river. • Formed when a meander migrated from side to side causing, the valley sides to erode and become wider. This creates a wide valley floor. • During a period of floods, silt is deposited on the floodplain and builds up layers of fertile land. **Level 2 (Clear) 3–4 marks:** • AO2 Shows clear understanding of how floodplains are formed. • AO3 Demonstrates application of knowledge and understanding to make a full interpretation of the photograph, suggesting how floodplains are formed. **Level 1 (Basic) 1–2 marks:** • AO2 Shows limited understanding of how flood plains are formed. • AO3 Demonstrates application of knowledge and understanding to make limited interpretation of photo suggesting possible reasons for the formation of floodplains. • 0 marks: No relevant content.	4

Physical landscapes in the UK: Glacial landscapes in the UK		
Question	**Marking guidance**	**Total marks**
1	Arête	1
2a	 **Figure 6**	4
2b	One of: • hanging valley • pyramidal peak • corrie.	1
3	**Indicative content** • Drumlins are smooth egg-shaped hills formed by glacial deposition. • Drumlins are made of moraine deposited by a glacier. • They have a streamlined shape created by the ice shaping them as it moved over the moraine to give a blunt end up the valley and a sharp end pointing down the valley. This shows the direction of the glacier's movement. • They can be found on the floor of a glacial trough. **Level 2 (Clear) 3–4 marks:** • AO2 Shows clear understanding of how drumlins are formed. • AO3 Demonstrates application of knowledge and understanding that is sound with clear interpretation of processes involved. **Level 1 (Basic) 1–2 marks:** • AO2 Shows limited understanding of how drumlins are formed. • AO3 Demonstrates application of knowledge and understanding is limited with basic interpretation of processes involved. • 0 marks: No relevant content.	4
4	**Indicative content** Includes any two from a range of economic activities in glacial areas. There is a range of economic activities in glacial areas and the response should include any two of the following activities: • Farming: upland areas have thin acidic soils due to glaciation so are good for sheep farming. • Farming: lowland glacial areas have a thick layer of till making it good for arable farming, e.g. East Anglia. • Forestry: coniferous trees cope well with the acidic soils in upland, e.g. in Scotland. • Quarrying: upland glaciated areas are often made of hard resistant rock. This is good for being crushed and used for stone in the building industry, e.g. limestone from the Pennine Hills. • Tourism: glacial uplands create stunning scenery. This provides excellent tourist opportunities, e.g. the Lake District where tourists spend approximately £1100 million every year. • Tourism: glacial uplands often provide excellent skiing opportunities, providing many jobs, e.g. in hotels, shops and other tertiary services. **Level 2 (Clear) 3–4 marks:** • AO2 Shows clear understanding of how economic activities have developed in upland glaciated areas. • AO3 Demonstrates application of knowledge and understanding that is sound with clear interpretation of economic activities involved. **Level 1 (Basic) 1–2 marks:** • AO2 Shows limited understanding of how economic activities have developed in upland areas. • AO3 Demonstrates application of knowledge and understanding that is limited with basic interpretation of economic activities involved. • 0 marks: No relevant content.	4

Urban issues and challenges: Global patterns of urban change		
Question	**Marking guidance**	**Total marks**
1	One mark for each correct answer: **B** The population of the world experienced a rapid growth from 1960. **C** Global population is predicted to rise to 9 billion by 2050. No credit if three or more answers are shaded.	2
2	• Process 1: Natural increase (1) when the birth rate exceeds the death rate (1). • Process 2: Migration (1) when immigration exceeds emigration in an area (1).	4
3	Two of the following points. • majority of the world's megacities are located in LICs or NEEs • most found in Asia • only five in developed countries • only two in Africa • only one in Europe and none in Oceania • more in the northern hemisphere.	2

4	1950 urban population = approximately 800 million 2050 estimated urban population = approximately 6300 million, so increase is approximately 5500 million or 5.5 billion. Accept range of 5.4 to 5.6 billion.	1
5	**Indicative content** Increase in urban population due to: • rural to urban migration • pull factors encouraging people to move to the cities: better opportunities in urban areas, e.g. jobs, education, health care, infrastructure, housing, etc. • TNCs have increased employment opportunities mostly in the cities • younger people most likely to migrate and are more likely to be most fertile and have a family • rates of urban growth fastest in NEEs/LICs where rural to urban migration is most rapid. Decrease in rural population due to: • push factors forcing people to leave the countryside, e.g. lack of jobs • lack of public services, schools, health care, housing, etc. • lack of money from subsistence farming • drought/crop failure • natural disasters • older people left behind, who are no longer fertile or having a family. **Level 3 (Detailed) 5–6 marks:** • AO3 Demonstrates thorough application of knowledge and understanding to give detailed explanations of reasons for a global increase in population. • AO3 Shows full understanding of both migration and natural increase as reasons for growth in global population in urban areas. Will give some explanation of differences between HICs, NEEs and LICs. **Level 2 (Clear) 3–4 marks:** • AO1 Demonstrates specific and accurate knowledge of reasons for growth in global urban population. • AO2 Shows clear geographical understanding of both migration and natural increase as reasons for growth in global population in urban areas. May recognise the differences between HICs, NEEs and LICs. **Level 1 (Basic) 1–2 marks:** • AO1 Demonstrates some knowledge of reasons for growth in global urban population. • AO2 Shows limited geographical understanding of the different reasons, with a focus on migration or natural increase. • 0 marks: No relevant content.	6

Urban issues and challenges: Urban growth in LICs and NEEs		
Question	**Marking guidance**	**Total marks**
1	Requires two separate points with elaboration. Any two advantages from: • coastal location, with five ports for import and export • centre of culture in Brazil with museums and world-famous carnival • centre for tourism with its beaches and mountainous surroundings, and is a UNESCO World Heritage Site • centre in Brazil for service and manufacturing industries.	4
2	**Indicative content** Informal economy • low paid • no job security • no benefits such as sick leave • no workers' employee rights • no tax paid to the government so doesn't benefit the people in the long term with services such as health and education. **Level 2 (Clear) 3–4 marks:** • AO2 Shows clear understanding of how informal economy creates problems. • AO3 Application is sound with clear interpretation of problems for people in LIC or NEE cities. **Level 1 (Basic) 1–2 marks:** • AO2 Shows limited understanding of how the informal sector economy creates problems. • AO3 Application is limited with basic interpretation of what informal economy is and how it can create problems for people. • 0 marks: No relevant content.	4
3	**Labels may include:** • Open sewers are unhygienic and can attract rats, which spread disease. • Lack of clean running water leads to people drinking contaminated water from the rivers and becoming ill. • Houses (self-)built from wood, plastic sheeting and corrugated iron are unstable and could easily be destroyed in a flood or fire. • Houses are very crowded together with whole families of more than 10 people living in a single room. **Level 2 (Clear) 3–4 marks:** • AO2 Shows clear understanding of how living in a squatter settlement creates problems. • AO3 Application is sound with clear interpretation of evidence in the photograph. **Level 1 (Basic) 1–2 marks:** • AO2 Shows limited understanding of how living in a squatter settlement creates problems. • AO3 Application is limited with basic interpretation of evidence in the photograph. • 0 marks: No relevant content.	4
4	Car	1
5	One mark for each problem identified. One mark for the elaboration of each point. • Problem 1: Pollution, vehicle exhaust fumes, especially diesel engines, cause air pollution. This often creates smog which can lead to health problems such as asthma. • Problem 2: Congestion from volume of traffic and a lack of road awareness creating chaos on the streets.	4
Urban issues and challenges: Urban change in the UK		
Question	**Marking guidance**	**Total marks**
1	Include any two points of data from the chart for 1 mark each • Majority of the population are White British • Equal numbers of Black, South Asian and White other	2

Question	Marking guidance	Total marks
2	One mark each for two examples of cultural diversity. One mark each for an elaboration of how this benefits the community. • Areas such as Shoreditch in London have developed into eclectic areas with museums, art galleries, restaurants and pubs, and large amounts of ethnic diversity. • Cultural life has become enriched with a wide range of foods and restaurants from all over the world. • It has developed the economy in the leisure and entertainment industries. • Strong community spirit developed in ethnic groups with events such as the Notting Hill Carnival bringing together black African and Afro-Caribbean people in celebration and creating a major tourist attraction.	4
3	**Indicative content** • Richmond upon Thames has a higher quality of life and a lower level of deprivation than Newham. • On average, people in Richmond upon Thames live to be 83 years old compared to 77 years old in Newham (1). This indicates differences in health and lifestyle between Richmond upon Thames and Newham (1). • A higher percentage of pupils get five A*–C grades in Richmond upon Thames, at 70% compared to 57% in Newham (1) This could be: due to the quality of the schools in Richmond upon Thames (1); due to the differences in attitudes to education of the young people in Newham (1); due to more investment in education and schools in Richmond upon Thames. • People in Richmond upon Thames earn on average nearly twice the salary of people in Newham (1). This could be linked to levels of education, as fewer people in Newham have received higher education (1). More people in Richmond upon Thames are employed in professional positions, having been to university (1). **Level 2 (Clear) 3–4 marks:** • A02 Shows clear understanding of the differences between two boroughs. • A03 Application is sound with clear interpretation of evidence in the table. **Level 1 (Basic) 1–2 marks:** • A02 Shows limited understanding of the differences between two boroughs. • A03 Application is limited with basic interpretation of evidence in the table. • 0 marks: No relevant content.	4
4	Figure 9 shows the Olympic Park in Stratford. However, the student's answer will depend on the case study used. **Indicative content** Improvements in environmental quality as part of a regeneration project such as Newham included: • derelict and toxic old industrial land was cleaned and could be rebuilt on • waterways and canals cleaned of all pollution • parkland created and 4000 trees planted • new wildlife habitats created. Improvements in social quality as part of a regeneration project such as Newham included: • road and transport improvements • housing improvements. **Level 2 (Clear) 3–4 marks:** • A02 Shows clear understanding of how the environment has improved as a result of a regeneration project. • A03 Application is sound with clear interpretation of evidence in the picture and example used. **Level 1 (Basic) 1 mark:** • A02 Shows limited understanding of how the environment has improved as a result of a regeneration project. • A03 Application is limited with basic interpretation of evidence in the picture and example used. • 0 marks: No relevant content.	4

Urban issues and challenges: Urban sustainability in the UK		
Question	**Marking guidance**	**Total marks**
1	**D** Urban and rural areas both consume energy and resources to provide for the population living there. No credit for more than one answer shaded.	1
2	• Inputs such as – food, water, energy, resources, etc. • Outputs such as – water, sewage, pollution, etc.	2
3	Any two features from: • Green spaces (1) – creation of parkland to improve environmental quality (1). • Affordable housing (1) – with low rents to make housing affordable for local people (1). • Energy efficient housing (1) – with high levels of insulation, triple glazing and energy efficient appliances to reduce energy consumption and heat loss (1). • Transport provision (1) – bus routes, cycle lanes, car shares schemes to reduce reliance on individual cars (1). • Local services and facilities provided within community (1) – schools, health centre, and community centre (1).	4
4	**Indicative content** • Doesn't create any harmful CO_2, which causes global warming. • Improves pollution and smog levels in cities, which improves the health of people breathing in fumes. • Provides a form of fitness for the people. • Is a sociable activity to do with other people. • Encourages people to get out of their cars if safe cycle lanes are available. • Can be used as a way to reach an integrated transport system such as a train, tube or bus station. **Level 2 (Clear) 3–4 marks:** • A02 Shows clear understanding of sustainable transport strategies. • A03 Application is sound with clear interpretation of how cycling can be an important part of a sustainable transport strategy. **Level 1 (Basic) 1 mark:** • A02 Shows limited understanding of sustainable transport strategies. • A03 Application is limited with basic interpretation of how cycling is part of a sustainable transport strategy. • 0 marks: No relevant content.	4

<table>
<tr><td>5</td><td>The student needs to evaluate a scheme using a named case study, e.g. London or Bristol, and explain the strategies used.
Indicative content
This will vary depending on the example chosen but could include:
• integrated transport network linking all different transport methods together
• use of ticket systems like the Oyster card to make travel easier and cheaper
• developing use of cycle lanes to encourage more cycling
• use of bus lanes to speed up bus travel
• more frequent public transport services
• improvements to tube services and trains in London
• sustainable bus services – electric buses, Bristol's Poo Bus
• electric car charging points
• congestion charge in London
• ring roads to take traffic around city centre
• park-and-ride schemes to avoid going into city centre
Problems or failures of the schemes:
• cycle lanes can't be created on narrow roads
• cycle lanes have parked cars or trees in them so not useable
• crowding on public transport
• people still like the convenience of their cars.
Level 3 (Detailed) 5–6 marks:
• AO3 Demonstrates thorough application of knowledge and understanding to give detailed evaluation of the strategies to manage traffic congestion.
• AO3 Shows full understanding of a variety of schemes and gives named examples. Clearly shows the benefits and problems of such schemes.
• Offers a conclusion.
Level 2 (Clear) 3–4 marks:
• AO2 Demonstrates specific and accurate knowledge of two or more different strategies to manage traffic congestion.
• AO3 Shows clear geographical understanding to evaluate the success of schemes using at least one specific example.
Level 1 (Basic) 1 mark:
• AO1 Demonstrates some knowledge of strategies to manage traffic congestion.
• AO2 Shows limited geographical understanding of how successful different schemes have been and may not give a suitable example.
• 0 marks: No relevant content.</td><td>6</td></tr>
<tr><td>6</td><td>Two advantages from:
• Improve air quality (1), which benefits people as air is cleaner for breathing, improving health (1).
• Creates wildlife habitats (1) and regenerates species in urban areas (1).
• Creates social spaces (1) for people to improve the community and the social sustainability of an area. (1)</td><td>4</td></tr>
</table>

<table>
<tr><th colspan="3">The changing economic world: Economic development and quality of life</th></tr>
<tr><th>Question</th><th>Marking guidance</th><th>Total marks</th></tr>
<tr><td>1</td><td>Credit similarities and differences between South America and Africa. Two should be described or implied, such as:
• Africa has many more LIC countries than South America (1)
• South America only has two LICs while Africa has many (1)
• Neither continent has any HICs (1)
Credit relevant reference to named countries. No credit for descriptions of other continents or global pattern. Answer must also offer a comparison.</td><td>2</td></tr>
<tr><td>2</td><td>Credit one advantage only.
One mark for basic statement, such as:
• It shows how wealthy people are (1).
• It shows what people are getting paid for their work (1).
Two marks for developed idea, such as:
• It shows the wealth of people and to what extent they can improve their lives by spending money on their homes or services (2).
• It shows how much money people are earning and therefore how much taxes the government could be getting to spend on improving infrastructure (2).</td><td>2</td></tr>
<tr><td>3</td><td>Credit one disadvantage only.
One mark for basic statement, such as:
• It only considers social and economic indicators (1).
• It does not use equality (1).
Two marks for developed idea, such as:
• It does not take into account the state of the natural environment, which if damaged would make development unsustainable (2).
• The social factors that it includes do not consider gender inequalities or other inequalities such as wealth and ethnicity (2).</td><td>2</td></tr>
<tr><td>4</td><td>Indicative content
• Climate influences development over a long period of time, with greater development in cooler wetter areas (temperate zones).
• Where it is not too hot and not too cold with enough rain, crops grow better, so there is more food for people.
• There are fewer fatal diseases in cooler areas, as these thrive where it is hot, like the tropics, where many people die or are weakened by disease so they cannot work well.
• Hot and cold environments and drier climates are more difficult to work in. The human body cannot operate in extremes and therefore work is less efficient.
Level 2 (Clear) 3–4 marks:
• AO2 Shows sound understanding of one aspect of physical geography relevant to development.
• AO3 Demonstrates sound application of knowledge and understanding in explaining how the chosen aspect of physical geography has affected development.
Level 1 (Basic) 1–2 marks:
• AO2 Shows limited understanding of one aspect of physical geography relevant to development.
• AO3 Demonstrates limited application of knowledge and understanding in explaining how the chosen aspect of physical geography has affected development.
• 0 marks: No relevant content.</td><td>4</td></tr>
<tr><td>5</td><td>Haiti = 200 per 100 000 people.
USA = 3 per 100 000 people. So 200 – 3 = 197 per 100 000 people.</td><td>1</td></tr>
</table>

6	**Indicative content** • The answer must give reasons for differences; there is no credit available for description of the graph on its own. • The graph shows that HICs have the lowest TB cases and LICs have the highest, except for South Africa which has the highest level of TB. • HICs have a lot of money and have invested in health care systems, medicines and doctors, which keep the population healthier. • LICs are poor and do not have the money to invest in medical care and so people catch diseases more easily and are often not treated. • LICs are poor and people cannot afford medical care and treatment. • In LICs people live in poor conditions with lower levels of hygiene which allows TB to exist and spread. • South Africa may classify as a NEE economically but it is a country that has not invested in social infrastructure to improve all people's lives at work and at home. • LICs and NEEs may not be able to help people in remoter rural areas where TB rates can be higher. **Level 2 (Clear) 3–4 marks:** • AO2 Shows sound understanding of reasons for differences in cases of TB. • AO3 Demonstrates sound application of knowledge and understanding in explaining why the cases of TB vary. **Level 1 (Basic) 1–2 marks:** • AO2 Shows limited understanding of reasons for differences in cases of TB. • AO3 Demonstrates limited application of knowledge and understanding in explaining why the cases of TB vary. • 0 marks: No relevant content.	4
7	**Two** reasons should be given, such as: • People are not strong enough to work efficiently on farms; this creates less food supplies, which weakens people further. • People are not strong enough to work efficiently in factories, so productivity goes down and less money is made. • Children may not develop properly and cannot contribute to the economy as adults. • If people are unable to work properly and earn money they cannot pay taxes, so the government has less money to invest in infrastructure and services. No credit for vague statements such as: too weak to work; health is poor; low-paid jobs.	2

The changing economic world: Global development gap		
Question	**Marking guidance**	**Total marks**
1a	Responses must focus on the comparison. Statement may be backed by fact. • FDI outflows have increased greatly from Developing Asia while from Europe they have declined. • Developing Asia increased by \$133b while Europe declined by \$60b.	1
1b	Transition = \$63b and Africa = \$13b. 63 – 13 = **\$50b**	1
2	Credit **one** way only. One mark for basic statement, such as: • FDI provides jobs (1) • FDI helps the multiplier effect (1). Two marks for developed idea, such as: • FDI brings in investment and creates jobs and therefore creates income for the country (2). • FDI may bring factories into the country which will encourage the growth of linked industries, e.g. suppliers and services (2).	2
3	**One** expanded reason should be given, such as: • FDI may not reduce poverty because the amount of investment is too small to have a large impact, such as only employing a few people on low wages. • FDI may not reduce poverty because the TNC may take the profits made out of the country and not re-invest it to create economic growth locally. • FDI may not reduce poverty because the TNC uses components and supplies from abroad and so does not support local businesses and industries. No credit for vague statements such as: • doesn't make people richer; profits disappear • government gives too much money.	2
4a	2015 tourists = 3.7 m tourist arrivals and 2009 tourists = 2.75m. 3.7 – 2.75 = **0.95m** (allow 0.9m to 1.0m)	1
4b	Responses must focus on the comparison. Statement may be backed by fact. Only one response required. • Tourist arrivals increased steadily between 2009 and 2015 with minor fluctuations, while the income fell between 2009 and 2011 before increasing slowly after 2012. • Tourist income was highest in 2009 when arrivals were at their lowest, then as arrivals increased, income decreased until after 2012, the gap between arrivals and income has been increasing.	1
5	Credit **one** way only. One mark for basic statement, such as: • Tourism provides jobs for people (1). • Tourism money helps start the multiplier effect (1). Two marks for developed idea, such as: • Tourism brings money into the country, which gives the government tax money that it can spend on improving services such as education. (2). • Tourism provides many jobs and so gives people wages, these people then spend money in local shops and for local services which gives more people wages, which they can then spend on other things. In this way the cycle of poverty is broken (2).	2
6	One disadvantage for one mark, such as: • tourism may provide only seasonal employment (1). **One** expanded disadvantage should be given for two marks, such as: • Tourism may be a disadvantage because the country may not receive all of the money as the tourism TNCs take most of it, and the amount of money received can vary each year so income is unreliable (2). • Tourism may be a disadvantage because large numbers of people put pressures on infrastructure and the natural environment; if infrastructure cannot cope then pollution and damage to the natural environment may occur (2). • Tourism may be focused in one part of a country and other areas may not receive the benefits of tourist income at all, creating a wealth and quality of life division within the country (2). No credit for vague statements such as: doesn't benefit everyone; income is low; government favours tourist areas.	2

7	The question asks for justification as to whether or not there have been significant improvements to the quality of life of poor people in an LIC or NEE brought by industrial change. It requires agreement or disagreement with the statement backed by evidence. **Indicative content** • Economic and industrial development from agriculture to industry produces more money, which can be invested in improving infrastructure such as water and sanitation: these help to improve the health of people. • Secondary industries are able to provide better paid jobs than farming and so the wages of people increase beyond the poverty level of US$1.90 per day; with more money people are able to improve their living conditions – such as their homes. • Economic and industrial development may increase trade and external links but the LIC/NEE may not benefit, ending up with a negative trade balance so that the country gets into debt and has no money to improve infrastructure that would improve people's lives. • Industrial development may occur too fast so that environmental laws are not in place; this may lead to pollution of the natural environment which may affect the living conditions (e.g. the Ogoni in Nigeria affected by oil spills). **Level 3 (Detailed) 7–9 marks:** • A01 Demonstrates comprehensive and specific knowledge of industrial change and quality of life. • A02 Shows thorough and accurate geographical understanding of industrial change and quality of life. • A03 Demonstrates effective application of knowledge and understanding in making a judgement about the issues and reaching a substantiated conclusion. Justification is detailed and balanced. **Level 2 (Clear) 4–6 marks:** • A01 Demonstrates reasonable knowledge of industrial change and quality of life. • A02 Shows some geographical understanding of industrial change and quality of life. • A03 Includes reasonable application of knowledge and understanding in making a judgement about the issues and reaching a conclusion. Justification is clear and well supported. **Level 1 (Basic) 1–3 marks:** • A01 Demonstrates limited knowledge of industrial change and quality of life. • A02 Shows some geographical understanding of industrial change and quality of life. • A03 May either include limited application of knowledge and understanding in making a judgement about the issues or in reaching a conclusion. Justification is limited to one or more simple points. • 0 marks: No relevant content and judgement not made. **For SPaG marks, please see the table in Weather hazards above.**	9+3 SPaG

The changing economic world: Rapid economic development and change		
Question	**Marking guidance**	**Total marks**
1a	2004 = 2350 thousand of barrels per day, 2016 = 1750 thousand of barrels per day. 2350 – 1750 = **600** thousand barrels per day. (Allow 575 to 625.)	1
1b	Response must focus on the comparison. Statement may be backed by fact. Only **one** response required. • Between 2004 and 2007 oil production increased to a peak and then declined sharply to a lower level, while between 2007 and 2010 there was a steep decline followed by a rise. • Both time periods have fluctuations but most of the 2004 to 2007 time period is at a high level (over 2400 thousand barrels per day) while 2007 to 2010 has a sharp decline – even dipping below 1700 thousand barrels per day.	1
2	Credit **one** disadvantage only. Can be social or political. Should be linked to a named LIC/NEE country. Nigeria is used as an example in the RG. One mark for basic statement, such as: • Nigeria has ethnic divisions (1) • Nigeria has corrupt politicians (1). Two marks for developed idea, such as: • Nigeria has three main ethnic groups and several minor ones. Historically there has been social division between the main groups which has led to internal conflicts and held back improvements to the quality of life (2). • Nigeria has a lot of corruption at decision-making levels within the country; some of this is linked to oil wealth. Therefore decisions have not led to efficient use of the oil wealth and quality of life in many areas remains poor (2).	2
3	**Indicative content** • Nigeria had the advantages of grasslands for growing crops and rearing animals in the centre of the country and agroforestry/plantations in the southern tropical rainforests. However, income from these was relatively low when exported. • Nigeria has changed from a country largely dependent on agricultural products to an oil producer with recent expansion of secondary industries. • The discovery of oil offshore led to Nigeria becoming the world's 12th largest producer and brought in a lot of wealth from exports (oil makes up 91% of exports). • Oil is a finite resource and will run out; therefore some of the wealth has been invested in secondary industries, e.g. soap manufacturing, to provide jobs and alternative income for the future. Some TNCs have invested in the country (e.g. Unilever). **Level 2 (Clear) 3–4 marks:** • A02 Shows sound understanding of the changing industrial structure of an LIC/NEE. • A03 Demonstrates sound application of knowledge and understanding in explaining why the LIC/NEE industrial structure has changed. **Level 1 (Basic) 1–2 marks:** • A02 Shows limited understanding of the changing industrial structure of an LIC/NEE. • A03 Demonstrates limited application of knowledge and understanding in explaining why the LIC/NEE industrial structure has changed. • 0 marks: No relevant content	4

4	The question asks for justification as to whether or not international aid and trade are essential to the economic development of LIC or NEE countries. It requires agreement or disagreement with the statement, backed by evidence. **Indicative content** • Economic development may be brought about by several things, international aid and trade are just two of these, others include remittances from migrants, development of infrastructure, tourism, introducing intermediate technology, getting rid of debts, and encouraging microfinance loans. • International aid may take several forms; loans may be provided to help build expensive development schemes, or may be smaller scale from NGOs for bottom-up local schemes to improve the lives of people. Nigeria receives aid for social issues such as clean water, education and health care as it has large numbers of poor people and cannot help them all. • Trade brings in money to a country by selling goods and resources that other countries want to buy. For example, Nigeria has oil, which is in great demand, and so the country can make considerable amounts of money (supplying 2.7% of the world's oil); it is expected to become a world top 20 economic nation soon because of this. • However, international aid may create dependency on external help and large loans may lead to debt. Trade is also not always fair, especially where raw materials are being sold which fetch a lower price than processed goods (e.g. turning oil in petrol). In 2016, Nigeria had a negative trade balance. **Level 3 (Detailed) 7–9 marks:** • A01 Demonstrates comprehensive and specific knowledge of international aid and trade of an LIC/NEE. • A02 Shows thorough and accurate geographical understanding of international aid and trade of an LIC/NEE. • A03 Demonstrates effective application of knowledge and understanding in making a judgement about the issues and reaching a substantiated conclusion. Justification is detailed and balanced. **Level 2 (Clear) 4–6 marks:** • A01 Demonstrates reasonable knowledge of international aid and trade of an LIC/NEE. • A02 Shows some geographical understanding of international aid and trade of an LIC/NEE. • A03 Includes reasonable application of knowledge and understanding in making a judgement about the issues and reaching a conclusion. Justification is clear and well supported. **Level 1 (Basic) 1–3 marks:** • A01 Demonstrates limited knowledge of international aid and trade of an LIC/NEE. • A02 Shows some geographical understanding of international aid and trade of an LIC/NEE. • A03 May either include limited application of knowledge and understanding in making a judgement about the issues or in reaching a conclusion. Justification is limited to one or more simple points. • 0 marks: No relevant content and judgement not made. **For SPaG marks, please see the table in Weather hazards above.**	9+3SPaG

The changing economic world: Changes in the UK economy		
Question	**Marking guidance**	**Total marks**
1a	Credit similarities and differences between primary employment and tertiary employment. **Two** should be described or implied. Such as: • primary declines from high of 70% to about 10% (1) • tertiary increases from 10% to over 50% (1) • the changes show opposite trends (1). No credit for descriptions of other lines. Answer must also offer a comparison.	2
1b	**Two** reasons should be given, such as: • raw materials (resources) in the UK in short supply/running out so could not supply secondary industries • outdated machinery and inefficiency in industry meant that secondary industries could not compete with more modern industries abroad • competition from Germany, Japan and South Korea, etc., reduced export earnings and made UK industries less profitable causing closures. No credit for vague statements such as industry was old; Japan developed its industries; jobs lost.	2
2	**Indicative content** • The UK now has many tertiary businesses and growing quaternary sector, these depend on the use of information technology to maintain links with each other and worldwide. • London is a world financial centre. This has been possible due to the internet and mobile communications technologies, which enable links to be maintained throughout the world to customers and financial markets. Two million UK people are employed in the financial sector. • 1.3 million UK people work directly in the IT sector of the economy. • Businesses are free to locate anywhere in the UK as office work can just require access to the internet and computers, and people can even work from home. **Level 2 (Clear) 3–4 marks:** • A02 Shows sound understanding of the role of information technology in post-industrial UK. • A03 Demonstrates sound application of knowledge and understanding in explaining how information technology creates economic opportunities in the UK. **Level 1 (Basic) 1–2 marks:** • A02 Shows limited understanding of the role of information technology in post-industrial UK. • A03 Demonstrates limited application of knowledge and understanding in explaining how information technology creates economic opportunities in the UK. • 0 marks: No relevant content.	4

3	The question asks for agreement as to whether or not it is possible to have economic growth in the UK without significant damage to the physical environment. It requires agreement or disagreement with the statement, backed by evidence. **Indicative content** • Economic growth may bring more factories and greater demand for raw materials such as coal, rock, sand, gravel, oil and metals. All of these activities have potential to damage the land, water, air and ecosystems through emissions or extraction activities. • Power stations provide electricity and these may emit greenhouse gases or radioactive waste or spoil scenery, depending on the primary energy source. As economic growth takes place there is an increase in energy demand which increases the impacts. • Quarrying creates scars in the landscape, such as at Torr Quarry in Somerset. Natural vegetation has also been removed and run-off patterns changed, and there is dust and noise pollution. Due to demand this quarry is predicted to operate until 2040. • The damage from quarries can be repaired; at Torr Quarry the plans are to create new woodland and grassland areas and landscape the quarry to create natural rock features and a lake. • With stronger environmental laws, eco-friendly technologies and greater awareness of potential damage, the physical environment can be protected and damage reduced to below a significant level. A lot of economic growth is in the tertiary and quaternary sectors which require fewer raw materials, just electricity. **Level 3 (Detailed) 7–9 marks:** • AO1 Demonstrates comprehensive and specific knowledge of economic growth and damage to the natural/physical environment in the UK. • AO2 Shows thorough and accurate geographical understanding of economic growth and damage to the environment. • AO3 Demonstrates effective application of knowledge and understanding in making a judgement about the issues and reaching a substantiated conclusion. Justification is detailed and balanced. **Level 2 (Clear) 4–6 marks:** • AO1 Demonstrates reasonable knowledge of economic growth and damage to the natural/physical environment in the UK. • AO2 Shows some geographical understanding of economic growth and damage to the environment. • AO3 Includes reasonable application of knowledge and understanding in making a judgement about the issues and reaching a conclusion. Justification is clear and well supported. **Level 1 (Basic) 1–3 marks:** • AO1 Demonstrates limited knowledge of economic growth and damage to the natural/physical environment in the UK. • AO2 Shows some geographical understanding of economic growth and damage to the environment. • AO3 May either include limited application of knowledge and understanding in making a judgement about the issues or in reaching a conclusion. Justification is limited to one or more simple points. • 0 marks: No relevant content and judgement not made. **For SPaG marks, please see the table in Weather hazards above.**	9+3 SPaG

The challenge of resource management: Resource management		
Question	**Marking guidance**	**Total marks**
1	One valid reason should be given, such as: • New Zealand is on a plate boundary so magma is near the surface to provide heat • New Zealand is an HIC and therefore has the money and technology available to develop geothermal energy. No credit for vague statements such as: • has volcanoes • is a rich country.	1
2	Must be a description of distribution. Credit observations based on the map provided. One mark for basic description, such as: • more in northern hemisphere • most in areas with volcanoes. Second mark for developed point using detail from the map, such as: • Northern hemisphere areas such as USA, Iceland, Italy and Japan have a lot of geothermal energy, while South America and most of Africa have little. • Uses data from the map, e.g. the Asia Pacific region has the greatest amount of geothermal energy capacity installed at 4.81 GW. • Countries and regions with destructive plate boundaries such as New Zealand and South-East Asia have geothermal energy. • Countries and regions with constructive plate boundaries such as Iceland and Kenya have geothermal energy.	2
3	**Indicative content** • Candidates should apply their knowledge and understanding of the energy debate to emphasise the role of sustainable energy supplies. Use should be made of the Figure. • IceLink involves undersea electricity cables directly from Iceland to the rest of Europe, e.g. UK, Norway and Germany. Iceland produces electricity by using geothermal energy (over 500 MW installed) – a renewable and sustainable source. • The energy mix of most European countries, such as the UK, only includes a small proportion of renewable energy sources and still is heavily dependent on fossil fuels. There needs to be a greater diversification into renewables for the future for the benefit of the natural environment but also to achieve energy security. • Countries like Norway and the UK have depended on North Sea oil and natural gas in the past and energy diversification is needed. Most northerly European countries have more limited opportunities for solar energy, but do use wind energy. A geothermal energy source would be an important addition to the future energy mix. • Energy demands have been increasing in countries such as Germany due to growth of tertiary industries and consumers as more electrical gadgets are being used. • Imports of energy from Iceland would avoid some of the negative issues associated with developing renewable energy sources in the UK, such as bioenergy and solar farms using up cropland, and wind turbines spoiling the scenery and causing deaths of birds. **Level 3 (Detailed) 5–6 marks:** • AO3 Demonstrates thorough application of knowledge and understanding of the energy mix of Europe (HICs) or selected European countries. • AO3 Demonstrates thorough application of knowledge and understanding of sustainable energy supplies and an evaluation of why they are needed. **Level 2 (Clear) 3–4 marks):** • AO3 Demonstrates application of knowledge and understanding by making relevant points about the energy mix of Europe (HICs) or selected European countries. • AO2 Develops one or more points that are relevant to sustainable energy supplies and an awareness of its importance. **Level 1 (Basic) 1–2 marks:** • AO3 Demonstrates application of knowledge and understanding through a limited understanding of the energy mix of Europe. • AO2 Demonstrates limited development of one or two points about sustainable energy supplies. • 0 marks: No relevant content.	6
4	One mark for correctly drawn bar. Shading not essential to gain mark.	1
5	One mark for the correct answer. **D** The Solway/Tweed has the best water quality No credit if two or more answers are shaded.	1

6	Responses should make use of the figure in order to explain their reasons. Candidates should apply their knowledge and understanding in interpreting the resource. One mark for recognition of highland areas with greater rainfall, drier South-East, location of London and demand for water, i.e. source and demand areas. One mark for reasons that focus on the fact that the areas with water sources such as Kielder reservoir and the Lake District are some distance away from the major cities such as Manchester, Leeds, Birmingham and London where water demand is highest. Need a way of transferring water such as through a canal. One mark for the need to irrigate crops in the South-East. No credit for simply describing the map.	3

The challenge of resource management: Food		
Question	**Marking guidance**	**Total marks**
1	One mark for correct answer. **C** 2390–2620 calories No credit if two or more answers are shaded.	1
2	The focus of the question is on where the distribution of daily calorie intake per capita is high and where it is lower in South America. One mark for basic description from the map, such as: • there are some countries with high and some with very low • countries in the east and south are higher than those on the north, west and centre. Second mark for developing a point with detail from the map, such as: • There is one country (Brazil) with 3050–3270 calories in the east and two with 2850–3050 calories in the south (Argentina, Chile), while two countries are below 2170 calories – one in the centre (Bolivia). • The countries in the north and north-west have lower daily calories, such as three with 2390–2620 calories than those in south and east which have between 230 and 650 more calories per person per day. Names of countries not expected. No credit if wrong continent used or just listing of countries.	2
3	Two natural factors should be stated. These can be any physical/environmental factors on a large scale (for a country), such as: • climate (temperature, precipitation, sunlight, seasons) • water supply • rock type and soils • pests and diseases.	2
4	Two reasons should be given, such as: • World population has grown and so there are more people to feed. • People are getting wealthier, even in LICs and especially in NEEs, and therefore people are able to buy more food. • Food tastes change as wealth increases and so there is a higher demand for certain food products.	2
5	**Indicative content** • An understanding of food insecurity and its impacts should be indicated in the answer. Impacts include famine, undernutrition, soil erosion, rising prices, social unrest. • Responses should focus on the difficulties caused for poorer people by a selection of impacts. • Expect some development of at least one situation where there have been food insecurity issues for poorer people. • Famine means that people do not have enough food to live, and the poorest, such as subsistence farmers, will be affected first. LICs in semi-arid areas such as the Sahel are often affected (e.g. Somalia 2010–2012) and people die. • When there are food shortages, prices in markets go up and poorer people cannot afford to buy enough food for a balanced diet; people then become unhealthy and are too weak to fight off disease. Children also become stunted and their development restricted. • The difficulties may become long term if soils are eroded by overuse or poor land management, or it could cause social unrest and armed conflicts as groups try to secure access to food resources (e.g. South Sudan). **Level 3 (Detailed) 5–6 marks:** • AO2 Shows thorough understanding of the impacts caused by food insecurity. • AO2 Demonstrates in detail how these impacts cause difficulties for poorer people. **Level 2 (Clear) 3–4 marks:** • AO1 Demonstrates specific and accurate knowledge of food insecurity, perhaps in a selected location. • AO2 Shows sound understanding of the impacts caused by food insecurity. **Level 1 (Basic) 1–2 marks:** • AO1 Demonstrates limited knowledge of food insecurity, perhaps in a selected location. • AO2 Shows simple understanding of the impacts caused by food insecurity. • 0 marks: No relevant content.	6

The challenge of resource management: Water		
Question	**Marking guidance**	**Total marks**
1	One mark for correct answer. **D** Extremely high stress No credit if two or more answers are shaded.	1
2	The focus of the question is on distribution of water stress in China; where it is high and where it is lower. One mark for basic description from the map, such as: • water stress is extremely high in some places and does not exist in other places • water stress in parts of the north-east and east is higher than in the west and north. Second mark for developing a point with detail from the map, such as: • In the north-east the river basins of the Yongding He, Tuhai Hu, Liao He and Daliao have extremely high water stress levels and the water stress level in Huang He is high. • About half the country of China suffers from some level of water stress; with a quarter of the country, located in the central-east area, having low to medium stress and another quarter medium stress or above. This leaves the rest of the country, especially the west and coastal areas, with no water stress. No credit for wrong country or just listing of river basins.	2
3	Two reasons should be given, such as: • world population has grown and so more water is needed – water is essential for life • people are getting wealthier, even in LICs and especially in NEEs, and therefore people are demanding more water for different purposes • farming has expanded due to more food demand and so more water is needed for irrigation. Farming is the biggest user of water in the world.	2
4	Two reasons should be given, such as: • Rain soaks into the ground and this can be extracted through wells. However, if too much is taken out long-term supplies are reduced, so it is better to restrict how much is taken out. • In times of lower rainfall, the groundwater is not replenished and so supplies can run low; it is therefore necessary to control how much water is taken out of the ground so that there is always enough there for people in the future. • Recharging aquifers, such as in Arizona, can replace water that has been used to be ready for future periods of low rainfall and drought.	2

5	**Indicative content** • An understanding of water insecurity and its impacts should be indicated in the answer. Impacts include disease, pollution, food production, industrial output, disputes/conflict and social unrest. • Responses should focus on the difficulties caused for poorer people by a selection of impacts. Nearly 800 million people worldwide do not have access to safe water. • Expect some development of at least one situation where there have been water insecurity issues for poorer people. • Clean safe water may not exist for poorer people to use; their health is therefore affected by disease (e.g. cholera such as in Haiti after the earthquake and hurricane) and pollution (e.g. phosphates from farming). • If there is not enough water, then fields cannot be irrigated and crop yields will be lower or fail in a drought situation. When there are food shortages, prices in markets go up and poorer people cannot afford to buy enough food for a balanced diet, people then become unhealthy and are too weak to fight off disease. Children may also become stunted and their development restricted. • Factories may be forced to close if they do not have water for cooling machinery or processing; people lose their jobs and have no money. • Water is essential for life and people may fight over it, especially if a government tries to use it for other purposes so that the poor people do not get as much (e.g. upstream dam). **Level 3 (Detailed) 5–6 marks:** • AO2 Shows thorough understanding of the impacts caused by water insecurity. • AO2 Demonstrates in detail how these impacts cause difficulties for poorer people. **Level 2 (Clear) 3–4 marks:** • AO1 Demonstrates specific and accurate knowledge of water insecurity, perhaps in a selected location. • AO2 Shows sound understanding of the impacts caused by water insecurity. **Level 1 (Basic) 1–2 marks:** • AO1 Demonstrates limited knowledge of water insecurity, perhaps in a selected location. • AO2 Shows simple understanding of the impacts caused by water insecurity. • 0 marks: No relevant content.	6

The challenge of resource management: Energy		
Question	**Marking guidance**	**Total marks**
1	One mark for correct answer. **C** 40 = 59% No credit if two or more answers are shaded.	1
2	The focus of the question is on where the distribution of energy access and security is high and where it is lower in South America. One mark for basic description from the map, such as: • there are some countries with high and some with low performance levels • there is a random distribution pattern from high to quite low. Second mark for developing a point with detail from the map, such as: • There is one country (Colombia) in the high category over 80%, and three countries in each of the other categories apart from the lowest (0–19%) where there are none. • The countries are split evenly between the categories with no distinct geographical pattern. There are three between 60–79% (e.g. Brazil), three between 40–59% (e.g. Peru), and three between 20–39% (e.g. Venezuela). Only one country in the high category. Names of countries not expected. No credit if wrong continent used or just listing of countries.	2
3	Two reasons should be given, such as: • Insulating walls and roofs reduces energy demand for heating by preventing heat escaping, leaving more energy for the future. • Energy efficient appliances use less electricity so not as much needs to be generated by power stations so they use less fuel, saving more for the future. • People can fit solar panels to their roofs, which means that they can generate some of their own energy from a free renewable resource instead of using fossil fuels such as natural gas.	2
4	**Indicative content** • An understanding of energy insecurity and its impacts should be indicated in the answer. Impacts include: removing people, environmental damage, food production, industrial output, disputes/conflict and social unrest. • Responses should focus on the difficulties caused for poorer people by a selection of impacts. • Expect some development of at least one situation where there have been energy insecurity issues for poorer people. • As energy runs out, there are pressures to expand exploration, extraction and production. Some of the locations chosen for this impact on poorer people, such as the Inuit in the Arctic or the Nanti in Peru. Poorer people may be forced to move from their homes because of flooding behind an HEP dam, or pipeline construction. • When there are energy shortages prices go up and poorer people cannot afford to buy enough energy for their needs. This affects the quality of their life and small businesses such as workshops and crafts. • Factories may be forced to close if they do not have energy to operate; people lose their jobs and have no money. • Energy is regarded by many as a modern essential and there is a lot of money involved so people may fight over it; often it is the poor people who are caught in the middle of conflicts (e.g. Iraq). **Level 3 (Detailed) 5–6 marks:** • AO2 Shows thorough understanding of the impacts caused by energy insecurity. • AO2 Demonstrates in detail how these impacts cause difficulties for poorer people. **Level 2 (Clear) 3–4 marks:** • AO1 Demonstrates specific and accurate knowledge of energy insecurity, perhaps in a selected location. • AO2 Shows sound understanding of the impacts caused by energy insecurity. **Level 1 (Basic) 1–2 marks:** • AO1 Demonstrates limited knowledge of energy insecurity, perhaps in a selected location. • AO2 Shows simple understanding of the impacts caused by energy insecurity. • 0 marks: No relevant content.	6
5	Two reasons should be given, such as: • world population has grown and so therefore more energy is needed (e.g. for cooking, heating) • people are getting wealthier, even in LICs and especially in NEEs, and therefore people are demanding more energy for different purposes in their homes and lives (e.g. appliances, gadgets, cars) • industries and businesses are expanding as the world develops economically and all of these need energy for factories, offices and transport.	2

Answers to the practice papers are available online.
Visit: www.scholastic.co.uk/gcse

Acknowledgements

Text permissions

p.100: UK Government (Department of Transport) © Crown Copyright; p.101: Foster + Partners.

Photo permissions

p.11: Image by Robert A. Rohde, Global Warming Art, Creative Commons Attribution-Share Alike 3.0 Unported license; p.13: DarwelShots/Shutterstock.com; p.18: KYTan/Shutterstock.com; p.22: Galyna Andrushko/Shutterstock.com; p.25: Matthew Jacques/Shutterstock.com; p.27: © Crown copyright 2017 OS [licence number pending]; p.31: © Crown copyright 2017 OS [licence number pending]; p.32: Paul Briden/Shutterstock.com; p.33 (top): Chris Moody/Shutterstock.com; p.33 (bottom): Ilona Kryzhanivska/Shutterstock.com; p.39: iStockphoto/ranplett; p.42: Paolo Grandi/Shutterstock.com; p.45: © Chris Dorney/Dreamstime.com; p.71: iStockphoto/Tigeryan; p.75: DavidYoung/Shutterstock.com; p.76: Atlaspix/Shutterstock.com; p.77 (top): Dchauy/Shutterstock.com; p.77 (bottom): B Brown/Shutterstock.com; p.78: Gregory/Shutterstock.com; p.79 (top): © Crown copyright 2017 OS [licence number pending]; p.79 (bottom): JuliusKielaitis/Shutterstock.com; p.99: © Crown copyright 2017 OS [licence number pending]; p.100 (top): © Crown copyright 2017 OS [licence number pending]; p.100 (bottom) : © Crown copyright 2017 OS [licence number pending]; p.106 (left): Dan Cowling; p.106 (right): Walencienne/Shutterstock.com

Artwork permissions

p.19: Mongabay.com, © Rhett Butler 2017, data source: RAISG Amazon 2012 Protected Areas Indigenous Territories; p.30: Adapted from http://www.s-cool.co.uk/gifs/g-geo-rivers-dia15.gif; p.36 and 81: Data UN Population Division, 2005; p.47: Data World Bank; p.48: Wikipedia, LordToran; p.49: Data WTO; p.51: UNCTAD; p.52: Data Jamaica Tourist Office; p.54: www.tradingeconomics.com, Organisation of the Petroleum Exporting Countries; p.59: Main world map image: Geothermal Power Generation in the World 2010-2014 Update Report, Ruggero Bertani, Open Access, http://www.sciencedirect.com/science/journal/03756505/60; p.60: Data EC Report from the Commission to the European Parliament and the Council on the Implementation of the Water Framework Directive (2000/60/EC), Brussells 14 November 2012, http://ec.europa.eu/environment/water/water-framework/pdf/3rd_report/CWD-2012-379_EN-Vol3_UK.pdf; p.61: AECOM; p.62: ChartsBin statistics collector team 2011, Daily Calorie Intake Per Capita, ChartsBin.com, viewed 8th February, 2017, <http://chartsbin.com/view/1150>, data FAO Statistics Division 2010, Food Balance Sheets, Food and Agriculture Organization of the United Nations, Rome, Italy, viewed 17th March, 2011, http://faostat.fao.org/; p.64: World Resources Institute, http://www.wri.org/resources/charts-graphs/water-stress-country; p.66: World Economic Forum and Accenture analysis; p.68; EPA's Climate Change Indicators (2016); p.69: Goddard Institute for Space Studies (GISS) and Climate Research Unit (CRU), prepared by ProcessTrends.com, updated by globalissues.org, http://www.globalissues.org/article/233/climate-change-and-global-warming-introduction. Sources: GISS Surface Temperature Analysis, NASA, accessed January 25, 2015; Global temperature, 1800–2006, ProcessTrends.com, accessed October 27, 2009; p.70: Weather.gov, mapping by NASA WorldWind; p.73: Wet Tropics Images/Wet Tropics Management Authority–Rainforest Explorer; p.74: Data Mongabay.com, © Rhett Butler 2017; p.82: Urban Geography, Stentor Danielson, http://debitage.net/humangeography, Data CIA World Factbook; p.85 (top): Life expectancy at birth, both sexes, 2015, http://gamapserver.who.int/mapLibrary/Files/Maps/Global_LifeExpectancy_bothsexes_2015.png, reprinted with permission of WHO; p.85 (bottom): Data WTO; p.86: http://migrationsmap.net; p.87: Data ONS; p.89: © FAO 2014 Understanding hunger and malnutrition, http://www.fao.org/resources/infographics/infographics-details/en/c/238873/, accessed March 2017; p.90 (top): Data National Statistics: Energy Trends September 2016, United Kingdom Statistics Authority; p.90 (bottom): Department of Energy & Climate Change, UK Energy Statistics, 2015 & Q4 2015, Statistical Press Release, 31 March 2016, © Crown Copyright 2017 Open Government licence; p.91: DG Agriculture & Rural Development, Agri-food trade in 2014: EU-US interaction strengthened, page 23 © European Union, 2015; p.93: WRI Aqueduct, World Resources Institute; p.95: Source: Enerdata, https://yearbook.enerdata.net/#wind-solar-share-electricity-production.html; p.97 (top): Air transport, passengers carried, International Civil Aviation Organization, Civil Aviation Statistics of the World and ICAO staff estimates © 2016 The World Bank Group, All Rights Reserved; p.97 (bottom): Department for Transport, Transport Statistics Great Britain 2015, Open Government Licence v.3.0; p.98: Data Department for Transport, United Kingdom; p.99: Eurostat